Mind-bending Variety Puzzles
Volume 1
Wordplay, Logic Puzzles, Sudoku, Trivia and More!

._. . _.. ... ._. ._. .. _. __.

Mitchell H. Allen

PencilPaperParacosm.com

Mind-bending Variety Puzzles Volume 1
Copyright © 2022 by Mitchell H. Allen
PencilPaperParacosm.com

ISBN: 979-8-9864160-0-7

This book belongs to

Table of Contents

Table of Contents

Introduction

Welcome, dear reader, to a different kind of puzzle book. In addition to classic puzzles like Fill-ins, Word Searches, Sudoku and Cryptograms, you'll discover more than 50 original, hand-crafted puzzles, logic problems, anagram challenges and trivia quizzes. If you like variety, I think you'll enjoy this collection.

With the exception of the classics, the activities in this book are open-ended. You know how puzzle magazine instructions prohibit you from using proper nouns, slang, foreign words, hyphenated words and contractions? That's just silly. If your mind sees these words, they are just as valid as the words found in the Answers section. So, feel free to claim victory in any manner that suits your solving style.

Fair warning: the vocabulary throughout this book ranges from easy to challenging. Don't let the easy puzzles fool you and don't be discouraged by the obscure words.

Several puzzles give you at least two different ways to find their solutions. You should strive to find what may seem to be serendipitous connections between the clues and emerging answers: often, they were inserted intentionally, as a reward for people who "see" beneath the surface.

As a matter of fact, this entire book contains a Delphic lagniappe (mysterious gift given at time of purchase.) Similar to Easter eggs in software, this hidden puzzle is yours for the finding.

I wish to acknowledge all the sources of inspiration for this collection: my father, Hillard Allen, card-carrying member of the Dad Jokes Society and one of the most intrepid wordplay enthusiasts I know; my wife, Toni, for her fact-checking on the Brady Bunch trivia and for numerous suggestions; my children, who give me an excuse to keep making games, challenging them with riddles and torturing them with my corny jokes; the dozens of puzzle books and magazines that kept me entertained for years; Will Shortz, a famous puzzle creator, whose Letter Bank invention predates what I thought was my own creation (*Decisions, Decisions*); and, the Internet, without whose resources I wouldn't have attempted making this book.

I hope you enjoy these puzzles and activities as much as I enjoyed putting them together. Visit my website by scanning the QR code below or entering https://pencilpaperparacosm.com into your browser.

State School

Good morning, class. Pop quiz! Answer seven questions about the American states. This quiz will test your knowledge of trivia, cultural references, bad puns and counting.
Answers are on page 126.

1. Raising

2. Hannah

3. 2,000 pounds of laundry

4. Only state with a single syllable

5. State with the most o's in its name

6. Four official commonwealths

7. Four states that spell out a letter of the Greek alphabet somewhere in their names

Things That Have _____

The nine words on the left, when paired with the correct words on the right, form nine compound words or two-word phrases that have something specific in common.

The answers are on page 126.

JUMBO

NIGHT

BLUE

FRUIT

LADY

SPRUCE

WHITE

HORSE

YELLOW

bat	belly	bird
blood	bug	fingers
fly	goose	hawk
house	jay	jet
knuckle	mare	radish
salad	shrimp	up

Skeleton Crew

Each of these artists recorded or covered a song with a skeleton bone in the title. Can you name all of the song titles?

Answers are on page 126.

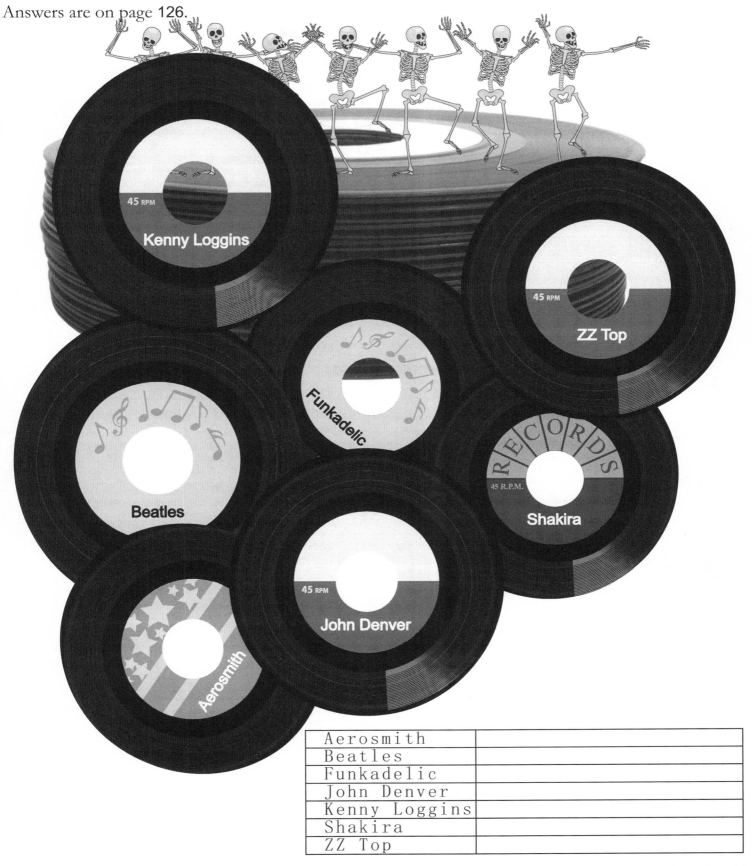

Aerosmith	
Beatles	
Funkadelic	
John Denver	
Kenny Loggins	
Shakira	
ZZ Top	

Ghosts in the Machine

Peek-a-boo! Can you find all of the spooky creatures in these devices? You don't have to use all of the letters in each word, but you will have to rearrange the letters that you do use. The first one is done for you.

Answers on page 126.

MONTGOLFIER   *GREMLIN* _____

SMARTPHONE   _____

RANDOMIZER   _____

TRINISCOPE   _____

NICKELODEON   _____

VIEWFINDER   _____

IMMOBILIZER   _____

SNOWPLOUGH   _____

Rack Your Brain

Sharpen your pencil! How many words can you make from the letter tiles below? Each rack is a separate puzzle.

You can only use a tile once per word. A list of words of at least fours letters appears on page 126, but feel free to write down 2- and 3-letter words, too.

D L R E T D O

A I P M D R Y

Skip to My Lou
"Lost my partner, what'll I do?" - Nat King Cole

A movie, a song and three guys walked into a dance hall…Can you match these partners to their Lou's?
Answer is on page 126.

1. La Bamba
2. "You'll Never Find Another Love Like Mine"
3. Bill Bixby
4. Bud Abbott
5. Ed Asner

Anagrams

Anagrams are made by rearranging letters in a word or phrase into other words and phrases. DECIMAL and CLAIMED are anagrams of MEDICAL. LOADING TRUCKS is one anagram for ROAST DUCKLING.

Unlike the *Rack Your Brain* puzzles, anagrams require that you use all of the letters in the word or phrase.

In the following puzzles, rearrange letters to uncover hidden messages, answer trivia questions and more. Sometimes, the only clues will be the title and a series of blank lines indicating how many answers are needed.

Answers are on page 126.

12 Signs of Opposition

RARE ALIBIS = _____ & _____

CURIOUS PASTOR = _____ & _____

IMAGINE GUITARISTS = _____ & _____

NICER CAR CON CARP = _____ & _____

AROUSE QUAIL = _____ & _____

GRIPS VOICES = _____ & _____

That's the Pits!

Answers are on page 126.

HOT SCAM

BARE CUBE

RAM

ORCA SPIT

OHMS

SO EVIL

RICH SEER

CHEAP

LUMP

TRANSIENCE

Write your answers here

Supreme Kart

Cricket City shoppers love the deals at the mega-store, Supreme Kart. While they pay cash for most purchases, Supreme Kart will accept trades for select items.

It turns out that the manager of Supreme Kart has a sense of humor. Once a month, she runs a promotion where shoppers can swap anything they own for merchandise that is an anagram of the item. Obviously, quantities are limited, so it's first-come, first-serve. (One lucky person traded some **Elk pics** for **pickles**.)

Will you be able to "cash in" on some of these deals? More importantly, which ones should you leave on the super market shelves?

Answers are on page 126..

Moose tat
Ripped lace
Boar's feet
Matte toner
Old army bed
Tube wetters
Bent-up oars
Tattered bowl
Cob bar trays
Idle silk mop
Rusted mangers
Glassed drains
Fur bride suit
Scab thickeners
Eel-faced turtle
Ersatz pullet ends
Huge armpit baster
Porous teeth rakes

Wild Weekend at Westville U.

Cricket City residents endured Westville University's homecoming weekend. The home team lost their match. During halftime, the marching band was uncoordinated and immature frat boys threw rolls of toilet paper onto the field in protest. This resulted in a game-delaying brouhaha in the stands.

Unfortunately, news coverage was a mess, too! Drunk reporters filed incoherent stories that had the editors in tears. While you can't do anything about events in the stadium, perhaps you can salvage the local newspaper before tomorrow's edition goes to print. Can you find 12 scrambled bits of text among the headlines, articles and image captions?

Answers are on page 126.

1.

2.

3.

4.

5.

6.

7.

8.

9.

10.

11.

12.

Cricket City Courier

Warblers arrested after stadium melee

Westville University's echoing mom was marred by fighting during the annual football game. Fans, angered by the charming band's poor race from pen during halftime, threw toilet paper onto the field. Alumni and other students confronted the trouble-makers. Fighting broke out in the stands after one young man pushed another into the screaming crowd.

Campus security personnel converged on the scene and arrested the genie people.

Dean Harvey Halston ordered the concession stand to stop selling beer. "Clearly, these gurney sots can't hold their liquor," hiccupped the inebriated dean.

Band member quits

Emma Sledgehammer claims toilet paper roll knocked her unconscious. Officials retort, "Ms. Sledgehammer has always been a bit of a minor panda. Didn't she also quit the here declare squad?"

The Cricket City League of Bad Bowlers welcomed Sledgehammer with peon rams.

Warthogs drop 10th straight game 35 - 33

In what has become a familiar litany, Coach Moe whines about the latest Warthog loss.

Davis bum elf at 2-yard line

"We never should have been in that position, we should have won. But we didn't. We lost, again. It hurts because all of these kids spent four weeks training for nothing. This should have been their moment, the first team to win. We were too close. We were on the two yard line with two minutes left and we were overconfident. We should have known that these kids wouldn't let us win this game. We should have just backed the kill."

In reality, all the Warthogs had to do was execute their signature wideout fade. "Stretch" Davis, at 7' 3", was beating coverage all game. The fact that Coach Moe didn't trust his racquet bark to complete a simple pass says more about his coaching ability than any of the players.

Neither Davis nor the senior QB had a comment. However. Vinny Sledgehammer, the Warthog's placekicker, grumbled about the lack of respect shown him and the kicking team.

Coach Moe was fired after the game.

Language professor invents filler - claims Latin not "dead"

Lorem ipsum dolor sit amet, consectetur adipiscing elit. Suspendisse ullamcorper mattis arcu, sed accumsan ipsum iaculis at.

Cras ultrices vehicula fermentum. Integer ultrices vehicula sem, a suscipit nunc malesuada quis. Ut iaculis volutpat augue vitae fermentum.

Duis dapibus mi diam, sed pulvinar massa aliquet sed. Vestibulum ante ipsum primis in faucibus orci luctus et ultrices posuere cubilia curae; Nullam consectetur tellus vitae mi facilisis maximus. Etiam a sollicitudin nisl.

Indicatory

Flip through any decent dictionary and you'll find that each of the following words comes before all of its anagrams. Not only that, the words in the list have something in common.

Numbers in parentheses indicates how many anagrams exist for the word.

Answers are on page 126.

Level 1:
BEGIN (2)
BELOW (2)
FILOS (1)
GHOST (2)
GIMPY (1)
GORSY (1)
HORST (1)

Level 2:
ADEPT (3)
AGIST (3)
BEINS (2)
CHIMO (2)
CHIRT (2)
FINOS (2)
GLOPS (2)
KNOPS (2)
MOPSY (2)

Level 3:
ABORT (2)
ADIOS (2)
AHINT (2)
AMORT (1)
CHIKS (1)
CHIVY (1)
DEFIS (1)
FLORS (1)

Level 4:
CEILS (3)
DELOS (5)
DEMOS (3)
ELOPS (4)
FIRST (3)

Level 5:
ABERS (6)
ACERS (8)
DEILS (9)
DEIST (6)

Bonus:
What do these clue words have in common?

Ungodly Hour

Ten deities and an angel walk into a bar. The bartender tells them that he is about to close. Of course, this angers the gods (the angel just shrugs.) They force the bartender to determine their identities, using just eleven anagrammatic phrases for *ungodly hour*. On top of that, he has to serve drinks until he completes this task.

Can you help this poor man decipher the cryptic phrases? The angel feels sorry for the guy and provides a bit of help by identifying himself. Notice that each letter in *ungodly hour* is used once in each answer. Even if you can't solve the anagrams, the clues will help you match them to the beings.

Answers are on page 127.

Anubis

Athena

Gabriel

Ganga

(2 words) U--- --------   Erase with vigor

(3 words) N--, ---- ----   Agree, sacred teacher

Hermes

(3 words) G- --- ------   Leave to bill every 60 minutes

(4 words) O- ---, --- ---   Dash away, geezer!

(3 words) D- ---- -----   Throw babies

Leza

(3 words) L OUD HORN GUY   Noisy trumpeter

(3 words) Y-- ----, ----   Self-asphyxiated, almighty!

Odin

(3 words) H--- ---- ---   Brandish own firearm

Plutus

(3 words) O- ------- ---   Hail wild mongrel

(2 words) U----- -----   Secular calabash

Shiva

(3 words) R---- ---- --   Portly, homely harlot

The Temporal Lord

Venus

Jimmy vs. Peter

How well do you know the fictional photographers, Jimmy Olsen and Peter Parker? Listed below are 18 snippets of trivia. See if you can match each one to the correct character.

Answers are on page 127.

Arrowverse

Bartholomew

Benjamin

Chloe Sullivan

Daily Bugle

Daily Planet

Gwen Stacy

J. Jonah Jameson

Liz Allan

Lucy Lane

Marc McClure

Marvel Cinematic Universe

Mary Jane Watson

Metropolis

Midtown High School

Perry White

Tobey Maguire

Uncle Ben

**CKED UP

Using each letter pair exactly once, append the letters CKED UP and match the new phrase to the correct definition. The first one is done for you.

Answers are on page 127.

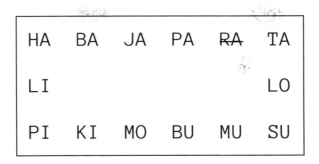

1. Accumulated   *RACKED UP*

2. Became Encouraged

3. Boxed

4. Bungled

5. Copied

6. Created a draft

7. Detected

8. Dismembered

9. Fastened

10. Inflicted damage upon

11. Lapped

12. Secured

13. Vacuumed

14. _____ a fuss

How to Solve Logic Puzzles

Many puzzles may be classified as logic puzzles, since they do require logic to solve them. Let's focus on logic grid puzzles, those word problems that require you to deduce truths from statements.

Often, such puzzles will be accompanied by a grid that is laid out in such a way as to aid you in keeping track of your logical deductions. While you don't have to use the grid, it can be helpful if you get stuck or if you're new to solving logic puzzles.

Before discussing the grid, let's talk about the types of clues you may find in a logic puzzle. Here is a typical scenario:

Three friends bought a different snack at the store (one was a bag of potato chips.) Each child paid with a single, different coin (one was a quarter.) Can you determine who bought which snack and how much was spent on each?

This logic puzzle scenario contains a number of important clues:

- Three children
- Three different snacks, one of which was a bag of potato chips
- Three different coins, one of which was a quarter

While that may seem obvious, the information in the scenario is often the only time a person or other item of information is mentioned. In general, these clues serve to tell you the relevant categories. When you see the corresponding grid, you will notice the categories.

		John	Mary	Ned	Dime	Quarter	Half dollar
Snack	Banana						
	Gummies						
	Potato chips						
Coin	Dime						
	Quarter						
	Half dollar						

The types of clues that follow the scenario range from simple to complex. Here are a few for our snack puzzle:

1. Ned bought a handful of gummies.
2. John is the only one who bought a healthy snack.
3. Mary spent the most money.
4. The banana cost more than the gummies but less than Mary's snack.

Clue number 1 is the simplest. Not only do you now know who bought the gummies, you also know who did not buy gummies. When using the grid, you indicate positive information by placing a dot, circle or check mark in the square that marks the intersection between the two known categories. Whenever you place a confirmation mark, you must place an X in the remaining squares of that row and column. This is how you eliminate choices that can't possibly be true.

Clue number 2 is pretty simple, although you have to determine which snack is considered a healthy snack. Fill in the grid to show that John bought the banana. Now, place X's in the Banana row and John column, as there can only be one positive mark in each row and column.

		John	Mary	Ned	Dime	Quarter	Half dollar
	Banana			x			
Snack	Gummies	x	x	·			
	Potato chips			x			
	Dime						
Coin	Quarter						
	Half dollar						

In this simple grid, it is clear that the only space left corresponds to Mary and potato chips. Go ahead and mark it.

All that remains is to determine who spent which coin. Clue number 3 is very simple: Mary spent the half dollar. Update your grid. But wait! Since we know what coin Mary used, we now know which coin was used to purchase the potato chips. Mark the rightmost square with a confirmation and fill in the appropriate X's. This method will come in very handy with more difficult puzzles.

Finally, clue number 4 gives us enough information to finish the puzzle. Can you figure it out? Yep, the banana cost a quarter and the gummies cost a dime.

Once you have discovered all of the relationships, you don't have to fill in the rest of the grid. Your grid should look like this:

		John	Mary	Ned	Dime	Quarter	Half dollar
Snack	Banana	·	x	x	x	·	x
	Gummies	x	x	·	·	x	x
	Potato chips	x	·	x	x	x	·
Coin	Dime		x				
	Quarter		x				
	Half dollar	x	·	x			

(Coin headers span John, Mary, Ned, Dime, Quarter, Half dollar)

Logic puzzles use many different types of statements to show relationships between categories in the scenario. With practice, you will learn to deduce information that isn't explicitly spelled out.

You should never make assumptions about the categories. In our sample puzzle, it is not correct to assume that a banana should cost more than a bag of chips, because the clues don't tell us that. While you're free to guess or to employ trial-and-error, just remember that logical deductions are all you need to solve logic puzzles.

You'll find several logic puzzles of various difficulty levels on the next few pages and throughout this book. Not all of them will have grids as a solving aid. Check out *Extracurricular Activities* (page 21), *Time is Money, But Money Saves Time* (page 34) and *Engine Engine #9* (page 70.)

Bear Necessities

Mama Bear, Papa Bear and Baby Bear had decided that it was silly to live in a house. However, each bear had grown attached to a different household item. In addition to these keepsakes, each bear was responsible for carrying a different essential tool to help them survive in the woods. From the clues, can you determine which keepsake and which essential tool was carried by each bear?

Answer and explanation are on page 127.

1. Mama Bear carried either the family photo or the frying pan.
2. Baby Bear carried the Goldilocks doll.
3. The bear who carried the reading glasses did not carry the frying pan or the shotgun.

	Family Photo	Reading glasses	Goldilocks doll	Fishing rod	Frying Pan	Shotgun
Mama Bear						
Papa Bear						
Baby Bear						
Fishing rod						
Frying Pan						
Shotgun						

Auction

The Cricket City Collectibles Club recently held an auction that raised exactly $1,000. Four items were sold. Each winning bidder spent a different amount and, coincidentally, each amount was a multiple of $100. From this information and the clues below, can you figure out who won each item and how much was paid for each? (A chart is provided, if you want to use it.)

Answer and explanation are on page 127.

1. Adam spent the most money.
2. The person who bought the autographed baseball card spent half as much as Colin, who spent half as much as the person who bought the rare Limoges antique plate.
3. Billy was not the one who bought the 1873 silver dollar.
4. The Limoges antique plate cost twice as much as the limited edition Ninja Fox action figure.

	Adam	Billy	Colin	Debbie	Amount Spent 100	200	300	400
Action Figure								
Antique Plate								
Baseball Card								
Silver Dollar								
Amount Spent 100								
200								
300								
400								

Extracurricular Activities

Dustin Barnett and his three siblings spend their weekday afternoons participating in at least one activity (one of which is piano.) From the clues, can you determine who does what and when?

Answer and explanation are on page 127.

1. No child participates in more than two different activities and no child shares an activity with a sibling.
2. The children who participate in multiple activities have practices on successive days.
3. Claire is the only child who doesn't play an instrument.
4. Vernon is a linebacker and plays guitar.
5. Instruments are only practiced on Tuesdays and Thursdays
6. Thursday is the only day when two different children are busy.
7. The child who plays the saxophone is the only one who does not participate in a sport.
8. Reba is the only child who practices on Mondays and Tuesdays.
9. Football practice is later in the week than soccer practice, but earlier in the week than gymnastics.

Weekday	Child	Activity
MONDAY		
TUESDAY		
WEDNESDAY		
THURSDAY		
THURSDAY		
FRIDAY		

Conspira-SEA

The Cricket City Conspiracy Club has an extensive library of "authentic" documents. Part of this collection, *The Origin Series*, claims to confirm the birthplace of nine legendary sea monsters. From the clues, can you determine the date of each document, as well as the sea monster featured in each?

Answer and explanation are on page 127.

1. The Hydra document and the Ross Sea document are dated over 100 years apart.
2. Five of the documents are the Sargasso Sea Diary, the one that features the Hydra, the one dated 1966, the 1971 Black Sea Report and the 1908 document about the Kraken.
3. The Yellow Sea document is dated either 1972 or 13 years after the Oman Sea document.
4. The Leviathan document was dated sometime before the Adriatic Sea File, and sometime after the Charybdis document.
5. Five of the monsters are Scylla and Charybdis, the one in the 1957 document, the one in the Red Sea document and the 2004 Ross Sea document.
6. Neither the Basking Shark nor the monster featured in the 1966 document is the Tyrrhenian Sea Terror.
7. Of the East China Dossier and the document featuring the Plesiosaur, one is dated 1957 and the other is dated 13 years before the document featuring Charybdis.
8. The document featuring the Basking Shark is dated sometime before the Red Sea document, which is dated sometime before 1971.
9. 38 years separates the Sargasso Sea and the Oman Sea documents. Neither document features the Kraken.
10. Of the Adriatic Sea File, the document featuring the Leviathan and the document featuring Cieren Croin, none is dated 1966.

A solving grid is on the next page, along with a place to record your answers.

Grid for Conspira-SEA

	1895	1908	1933	1946	1957	1966	1971	1972	2004	Basking Shark	Charybdis	Cirein Croin	Hydra	Kraken	Leviathan	Makara	Plesiosaur	Scylla
Adriatic Sea File																		
Black Sea Report																		
East China Sea Dossier																		
Oman Sea Monster																		
Red Sea Report																		
Ross Sea Papers																		
Sargasso Sea Diary																		
Tyrrhenian Sea Terror																		
Yellow Sea Sailor's Log																		
Basking Shark																		
Charybdis																		
Cirein Croin																		
Hydra																		
Kraken																		
Leviathan																		
Makara																		
Plesiosaur																		
Scylla																		

Date	Report Title	Monster
1895		
1908		
1933		
1946		
1957		
1966		
1971		
1972		
2004		

Easy As Pie!

The following pages have crossword-style puzzles known as Fill-ins. Most such puzzles help you by filling in one of the words. Only one of these puzzles provide a starting word. However, if there is only one word of a certain length in the list, you just have to find the corresponding blank spaces in the grid. Think of these as your starting words.

If two or more words could fit into the same blank spaces, you'll have to eliminate the ones that prevent the intersecting space(s) from being filled in. Speaking of spaces, don't leave a space between a two- or three- word phrase when placing them in the grid (**KEY LIME** becomes **KEYLIME**.)

Answers are on page 128.

5 Letters
APPLE
LEMON
PEACH

6 Letters
CHERRY

7 Letters
PUMPKIN

8 Letters
KEY LIME

9 Letters
BLUEBERRY
RASPBERRY

12 Letters
BANANA CREAM

Instruments of Torture

5 Letters
CELLO
FLUTE
KAZOO

6 Letters
VIOLIN

7 Letters
COW BELL
WHISTLE

8 Letters
BAGPIPES
CLARINET

9 Letters
ACCORDION
HARMONICA
VIBRASLAP

10 Letters
KETTLE DRUM

11 Letters
ENGLISH HORN
HARPSICHORD

12 Letters
BASS TROMBONE

13 Letters
DOUBLE BASSOON

14 Letters
ELECTRIC GUITAR

Hammerin' Hank

4 Letters
FOUL
RBIS
WALK

5 Letters
SLIDE
STEAL

6 Letters
BATTER
DOUBLE
RECORD
SINGLE
TRIPLE
UMPIRE

7 Letters
FLY BALL
HOMERUN
INNINGS
PITCHER
SLUGGER

8 Letters
BABE RUTH

9 Letters
CURVEBALL
FORTY-FOUR
PICKED OFF
GRAND SLAM
STRIKEOUT
WILD PITCH

10 Letters
BARRY BONDS
DOUBLE PLAY
HALL OF FAME
HENRY AARON

12 Letters
BATTING CHAMP
MAJOR LEAGUES
RIGHT FIELDER

13 Letters
ATLANTA BRAVES

14 Letters
SPRING TRAINING

Bob's Your Uncle

3 Letters	4 Letters	5 Letters	6 Letters
FIT	FLOG	DODGY	BLIMEY
GIT	MATE	GRASS	CHEEKY
GOB	NICK	JAMMY	~~CHEERS~~
KIP	NOWT	LOLLY	GAFFER
MUG	PRAT	MANKY	GUTTED
		MOGGY	MINTED
		SHIFT	NUMPTY
		SKINT	PUNTER
		TELLY	

Swift Response

6 Letters
CURTLY
NIMBLY
PRONTO

7 Letters
BRIEFLY
BRISKLY
LITHELY
LUSTILY
QUICKLY
RAPIDLY
SHORTLY

8 Letters
ABRUPTLY
ADROITLY
PROMPTLY

9 Letters
CURSORILY
EARNESTLY
FORTHWITH
HURRIEDLY
INSTANTLY
POSTHASTE
SUMMARILY

10 Letters
FLEETINGLY
TIMELESSLY

11 Letters
DEPTHLESSLY
IMMEDIATELY

12 Letters
EFFORTLESSLY
PROFICIENTLY

13 Letters
ENERGETICALLY
EXPEDITIOUSLY
PERFUNCTORILY

14 Letters
WHOLEHEARTEDLY

Famous Pigs

4 Letters
BABE

6 Letters
GUB-GUB
PIGLET
PUMBAA
WILBUR

7 Letters
MAXWELL
SALOMEY

8 Letters
NAPOLEON
OLD MAJOR
PEPPA PIG
PORKY PIG
SNOWBALL
SQUEALER

9 Letters
MISS PIGGY

10 Letters
PETUNIA PIG

11 Letters
PETER PORKER

12 Letters
GULLINBURSTI
PIGGLY WIGGLY

Fruit Fill

4 Letters
SLOE
5 Letters
MANGO
OLIVE

6 Letters
AJOWAN
FEIJOA
LUNGAN
LYCHEE
PAWPAW
PEPINO
POMELO

7 Letters
ATEMOYA
AVOCADO
KUMQUAT
TANGELO
8 Letters
BIGAROON
BREADNUT
HAGBERRY
MULBERRY
RAMBUTAN
SHADDOCK

9 Letters
AUBERGINE

Alarming Final

You must fill in the listed word *and* one or more anagrams for each word. The number of anagrams is in parentheses. To help you get started, **GAB** is the one anagram for Bag.

Answer is on page 128.

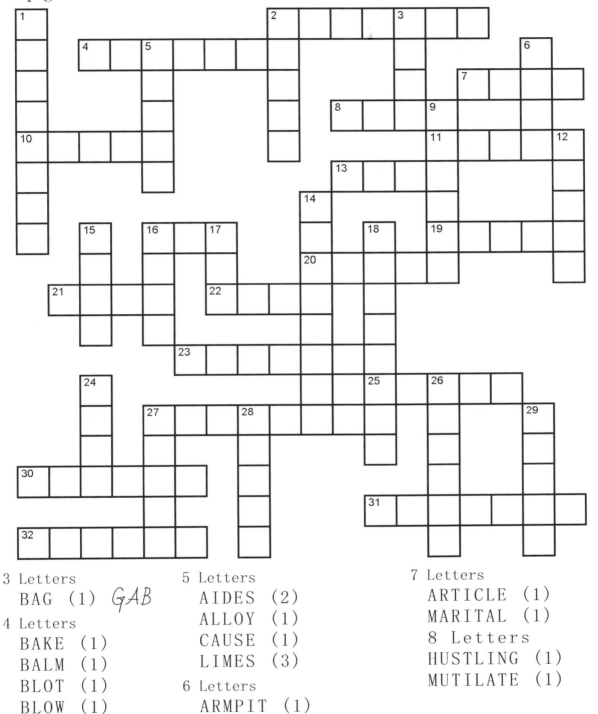

3 Letters
BAG (1) *GAB*

4 Letters
BAKE (1)
BALM (1)
BLOT (1)
BLOW (1)
CALM (1)

5 Letters
AIDES (2)
ALLOY (1)
CAUSE (1)
LIMES (3)

6 Letters
ARMPIT (1)
BATTLE (1)

7 Letters
ARTICLE (1)
MARITAL (1)

8 Letters
HUSTLING (1)
MUTILATE (1)

On the Cutting Edge

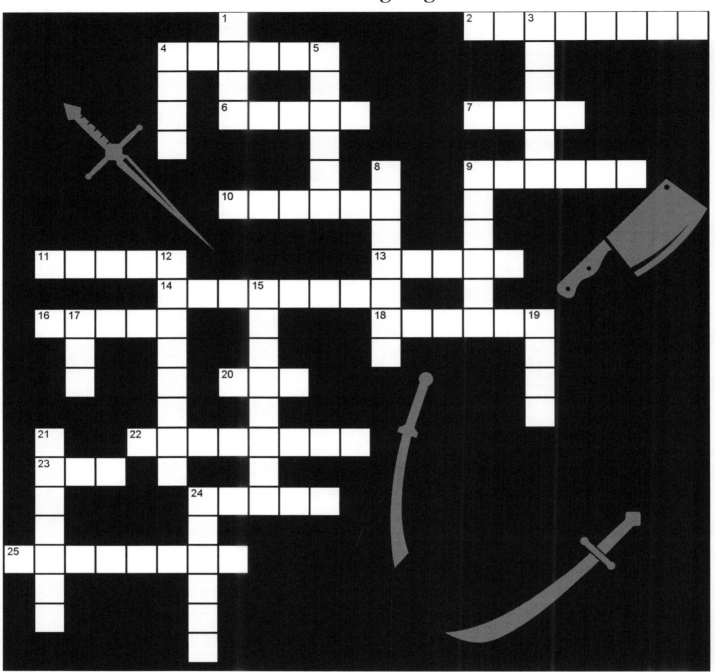

3 Letters
ADZ
ULU
ZAX

4 Letters
BOLO
EPEE
KRIS
SHIV

5 Letters
ANLAS
KUKRI
PANGA
SKEAN
TSUBA

6 Letters
ANLACE
BARLOW
BARONG
BILBOA
GLAIVE
PARANG
RAPIER
TOLEDO

7 Letters
CATLING
COUTEAU

8 Letters
BISTOURY
CLAYMORE
CURTALAX
FALCHION
SCIMITAR
YATAGHAN

Steampunk Contraption

In this special fill-in puzzle, try to chain together as many components as possible. Each component must fit between a pair of gears. No component may intersect with any other component. Do not leave a space between 2-word components.

A 9-piece monstrosity is on page 128.

3 Letters
COG

4 Letters
BOLT
COIL
GEAR
PLUG

5 Letters
GAUGE

6 Letters
BOILER
MAGNET
PISTON

7 Letters
AIRSHIP
GOGGLES
LANTERN
IRON KEY

8 Letters
GAS MASK

9 Letters
BLUEPRINT
STOP VALVE

10 Letters
CLOCKWORKS
CRANKSHAFT
PIPE WRENCH

11 Letters
STEAM ENGINE

12 Letters
IRONCLAD TANK
POTION BOTTLE

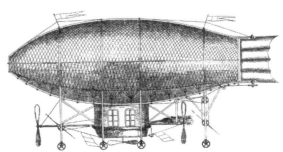

Time is Money, But Money Saves Time

Cinderella wants to go to the ball seven days from now. She needs a gown, shoes and carriage. Her budget is 100 silver coins. Although she can make a gown in four days, Cinderella needs all the help she can get. After talking to a few people, she receives several offers:

- Little Red Riding Hood will sell the material for a gown for 30 silver coins.
- Snow White will sell the material for a gown for 15 silver coins, as long as Cinderella also buys a pair of matching shoes for 5 silver coins.
- Her friend, Rapunzel, can make a gown in two days for 25 silver coins.
- The village shoemaker offers to make a pair of shoes for 10 silver coins.
- Jack, the giant-killer, offers to help any way he can, for 20 silver coins a day.
- Rumpelstiltskin offers to provide shoes and a carriage if Cinderella first travels to the enchanted forest to pluck magic mushrooms for two days. The forest is one day away. To sweeten the deal, Rumpelstiltskin will have his carriage take her to and from the forest.
- The Bibbidi-Bobbidi-Boo Livery Company rents carriages for 85 silver coins a night.

Which of the following scenarios will get her to the castle on time without overspending or buying unneeded things?

A) Cinderella buys the material and golden slippers from Snow White, makes her own gown and hires the Bibbidi-Bobbidi-Boo Livery Company.

B) Cinderella buys the material from Snow White, makes her own gown, agrees to Rumpelstiltskin's deal and pays Jack to make the mushroom run.

C) Cinderella buys the material from Red, makes her own gown and hires both the village shoemaker and the Bibbidi-Bobbidi-Boo Livery Company.

D) Cinderella buys the material from Snow White, makes her own gown and agrees to Rumpelstiltskin's deal.

E) Cinderella hires Rapunzel, the village shoemaker and the Bibbidi-Bobbidi-Boo Livery Company.

F) Cinderella buys the material from Red, makes her own gown and agrees to Rumpelstiltskin's deal.

G) Cinderella buys the material from Red, makes her own gown, agrees to Rumpelstiltskin's deal and pays Jack to make the mushroom run.

Answer is on page 129.

National Security Amnesia

Eight agents have forgotten where they work! Using the clues, can you determine which government agency employs each person? Each answer is a single word that includes one of the following acronyms: **ATF, CIA, DEA, DIA, DOJ, FBI, ICE, NSA,** or **TSA**. The agency letters appear exactly as shown, but may be at the beginning, end or somewhere within the word. For example, PUF**FBI**RD. (Agent #1 doesn't suffer from amnesia.)

Answers are on page 129.

1. An American Pacific shorebird
2. Two times
3. To emit rays
4. Martial arts school
5. Painful experience
6. Raised floor for speakers
7. Ship's wreckage
8. Mentally unsound
9. David Blaine, for one

Agent #1

PUFFBIRD

Agent #2

Agent #3

Agent #4

Agent #5

Agent #6

Agent #7

Agent #8

Agent #9

It's a Numbers Game

You've bought a board game at a yard sale. When you open the box, you find a musty board, a dried-out erasable marker and ten smudged tokens. The rules booklet is not in English; however, the pictures suggest that you write a number on each token before placing them on the board.

Can you figure out what those numbers might be and where you would place them?

One possibility is on page 129.

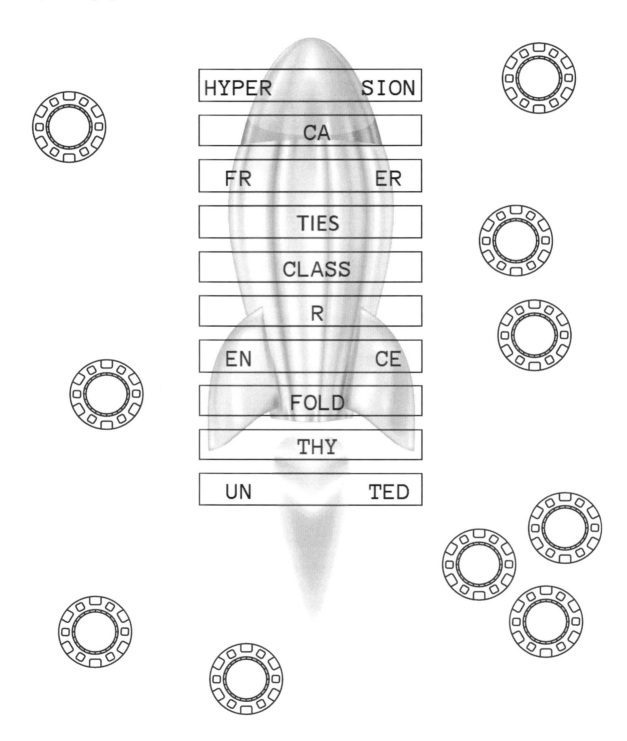

Homework Helpers

Four students, including Brad, waited until the last minute to do their high school chemistry experiments for their term papers. They resorted to unethical methods to turn in their papers with the rest of the class. The teacher discovered three of the four cheaters. The dean took swift action, including expelling one student. From this information and the following clues, can you determine who got away with cheating? (You *don't* have to figure out everything else.)

Answer and explanation are on page 129.

1. Of the two boys, one used Google Translate and the other used Wikipedia.
2. The two students who received an F were punished.
3. The student who used Wikipedia received a C and automatically failed the class when the teacher discovered the ruse.
4. Angela received a lower grade than the student who wrote the Kinetic Reduction paper and a higher grade than the student who hired a writer.

		Angela	Brad	Chelsea	Daniel	Expelled	Failed class	Never Caught	Suspended	Grade: C	Grade: D	Grade: F	Grade: F	Google Translate	Hired a writer	Plagiarized	Wikipedia
Experiment	Kinetic Reduction																
	Nonpolar Adsorption																
	Proton Oscillation																
	Solvent Bombardment																
Helper	Google Translate																
	Hired a writer																
	Plagiarized																
	Wikipedia																
Grade	Grade: C																
	Grade: D																
	Grade: F																
	Grade: F																
Consequence	Expelled																
	Failed class																
	Never Caught																
	Suspended																

Match Wits

In this challenge, you must find 16 ten-letter words. You can do it the hard way or the impossible way!

Hard Way

Solve 32 clues and pair them using three rules: one clue will be a four-letter word, the other clue will be a six-letter word; both words will begin with the same letter; append the six-letter word to the four-letter word to form the ten-letter word.

Impossible Way

Decipher the deliberately vague clues for each ten-letter word.

Answers are on page 129.

	4 letters	6 letters	
1. Difficult			Going Toward
2. Choose			Secure a tip
3. Golf cry			Blame
4. Alight			Barricaded
5. Riser			Nun
6. Arraign			Three-ring
7. Worker			Stinging sensation
8. Copse			Temp
9. Fortune-teller			Fortune-teller's client?
10. Bringing Up Baby?			Texas lawman
11. Show fangs			Endorsed
12. Deficiency			Radiance
13. Flank			Snatches
14. Binary, for example			Lebron, on-court
15. Banana peel mishap			Firth
16. Lullaby			Belabor

Clues for ten-letter words

1. Mulish
2. Defalcator
3. Pollicus' neighbor
4. Noncoastal
5. Cinderella's nemesis
6. Bibliopegist
7. In a fetching manner
8. Cabinetmaker
9. Railroad stripe
10. Shuffler
11. Sans Saddle
12. Not Energetic
13. Hits obliquely
14. A pitching profession
15. Tailgate at the Indy 500
16. Whitney Houston was one

Oh, My Nose!

Test your knowledge of the iconic 70's sit-com, *The Brady Bunch*.
Answers on page 129.

1. Which character was in each square during the opening credits?

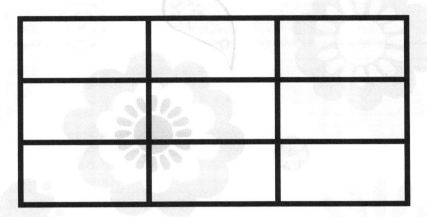

2. What was Mike's profession?

3. Who was Alice's boyfriend and what was his profession?

4. Where did Bobby and Cindy get lost?

5. What historical figure was Peter supposed to portray in the school play?

6. Who was Jan's imaginary boyfriend?

7. "What's for dinner, Alice?"

8. On what presidential street did the Brady's live?

9. Which Brady got fired from which two jobs?

10. What was Carol's full name? (Extra credit: what was Mike's middle name?)

11. Four main characters also had different roles in different episodes, can you name the characters and the other roles? (For extra credit, name the episodes.)

Bonus: What connections did The Brady Bunch share with Gilligan's Island?

Cryptograms

A cryptogram is a coded message. The code is derived from substituting one letter for another. For example, **Y FKZC SW WKPDYC** is a cryptogram for I LOVE MY YORKIE. The same letter substitution is kept throughout the message. So once you decide that **Y** was substituted for I, you can change all of the other **Y**'s to I's. Each message has its own code.

If you've never tried cryptograms, here are a few helpful tips. Since I and A are the only common single-letter words in English, try those if the message has single letters in it. Try to figure out other short words before tackling longer ones. Look for contractions, such as DOESN'T. The most frequently used letters in English words are E, T, A, O, N, R, I, S and H. Use a pencil with a good eraser!

A variety of coded messages await your solving skills: quotes, lists, jokes and random nonsense. The answers can be found on pages 129-130.

1. "OG ONWEJT'Z HNMJ EIZ IHVIGZ UJJF I ZQZWISFSFY DNTAJ DNT NQT

   DIOSHG, IFB NFJ ND OG YTJIWJZW PNGZ SZ ZJJSFY EJT SFWJYTSWG,

   EJT ANOXIZZSNF, EJT SFWJHHSYJFAJ TJDHJAWJB SF OG BIQYEWJTZ."

   – OSAEJHHJ NUIOI

2. "G YKVJ NGU FGU TJGAU NMAJ LAMN G LMMTKVR EDJVCKMU CRGU G

   LMMT FGU TJGAU LAMN G YKVJ GUVYJA."

   – XADFJ TJJ

3. "D KXMQ YZ QZ YCM SMPY SZL. P ONDMGQ ZO ADGM, CM HPX YCM

   NPJJMN PGQ POYMN, HM'Q SM QZDGE P SRZTB JPNYI ZN XZAMYCDGE

   ZN P CZKXM JPNYI, PGQ CM'X EMYYDG' PRR YCM PYYMGYDZG PGQ

   D'Q MGQ KJ HDYC P CPGQOKR ZO XJDY, IZK BGZH, ONZA QZDGE

   YCM SMPYX."

   – QAL

Cryptograms - continued

4. "GX OZT ZWZQGYP XUZX Z KDZF XUZX TAAWT SZXAS GY XUGT

OMCDS... Z WZY OUMTA EATX ICGAYS GT Z TGN—IMMX OUGXA

CZEEGX... EVX GX RZVPUX MY, ATKARGZDDF OGXU FMVYP KAMKDA —

XUAF TVCKCGTAS WA WMTX MI ZDD."

— LZWAT TXAOZCX

5. "MZ OP KPL HZCZCIZH OJVR, MZ HZCZCIZH CPCZKLR."

— SZRJHZ DJYZRZ

6. "PMWZB 'WVZ TPWBHG,' H UPJJEW LZPB YQJSOPYYZY. PY YEEJ PY H

AQW WVZT EJ, AZEAOZ BZUESJHDZ TZ."

— UPBBHZ—PJJZ TEYY

7. "FZ GET ZEHLRQ BXSPLUZ E GKLRM FKX LH EBSELM XB JKZ MESI;

JKZ SZER JSEPZMQ XB RLBZ LH FKZT VZT ESZ EBSELM XB JKZ RLPKJ."

— AREJX

8. "CWFJF'T, YPSF, L ZLJS MFFZYF DJ L MLPY CWLC YPIFT LC CWF

RLOS DH LYY DH DAJ WFLZT, LMZ CWLC'T EDAJ HFLJ."

— TLMZJL DW

9. "RBYJAQZ, PCYOBJC BJY HQCTVRBTI OUBT, VUTTAJ XC DTFBWCP, XDJ

    BG GUVCP HBJR VADQUIC, TCCP TAJ XC FBWCP UIUBT."

    — EUZU UTICFAD

10. "XJUK VSA QSGU NSBUSKU, RJU EUNR RJFKC VSA MIK STTUZ FN

    VSAZ WZUNUKMU. JSX MIK VSA QSGU FT VSA IZU KSR RJUZU?"

    — RJFMJ KJIR JIKJ

11. "NOOK QZDX ACGO CVTCQE YZTCXF YSO EDJESMJO — CJF ESCFZTE

    TMVV ACVV UOSMJF QZD."

    — TCVY TSMYHCJ

12. ZW GTAJU QJ R KUAURC MQCCUA. GU FTUJ YGATVFG YGAUU XTVPSJ

    TH TRYJ UOUAW SRW.

13. Z AEPH MG ZL BXP IUEPTBT UI LUEBXPEL DFKZIUELZF. QUTB UI QN

    IEZPLJT FEP FKTU BEPPT, TU NUM QZAXB TFN Z FQ GUGKFE.

14. HGR ZFHEXTZSHF XT HGR PTHRETZHPXTZC FVZMR FHZHPXT VERKRE HX

    FPV MXFWXF ZTJ RZH WPCLD YZD MZTJD IZEF.

15. "ICW YDEF FVB HCCE? RWNF NDI FVB YCJP DEP A'QQ FVJCY D

    QDNNC DJCWEP AF DEP OWQQ AF PCYE."

    —KBCJKB MDAQBI AE AF'N D YCEPBJLWQ QALB

16. PEEKABOO IEWOR AL LBGH KE WCRLTGKBCR XP KZL TWOLG RXRC'K

    UZBCML BOO KZL KXYL.

17. C TQNKMDL JCGME YA XI C ONNX CLU ECRE, "GNXXYVN ZCMN

    ZYEDV." EI XQNR XYKLNU DLXI C ADVVIGI CLU C UKYZ.

18. "VBQPIGTO BPV GTEQTWQC PV P KZNLIZNGVQ MQWBQQT IFTTGTO PBPD

    PTC XGOAWGTO."

    — XGTRQD LQWQI CFTTQ

19. B VAUWNM, B ABRRU BTH B SUTUNMWA LBOF UTMY B RBA. MDW

    RBAMWTHWA OYYFN BM MDWS BTH NBGN, "LDBM UN MDUN — B CYFW?"

20. N RNU LNDACI SUYK N JNE LSYX XSB NDDSVNYKE NUI NBACI YXC

    JNEYCUICE, "IK MKP BCETC DNLMCEB XCEC?" "BPEC IK," ECODSCI

    YXC JNEYCUICE. "VKKI," BNSI YXC RNU. "VSTC RC N JCCE, NUI

    S'DD XNTC N DNLMCE HKE RM VNYKE."

21. "YES ELHR BLHY LDGZY DSTCI L DLHYSCRSH TA JTIZHTCI GZY PEG

    TA RHZCM LCR PEG TA NZAY AYZBTR."

    — HTKELHR DHLZCAYSTC

22. "DML DAXKPFL IEDM MYSEQH YQ XNLQ ZEQT, XG JXKAWL, EW DMYD

NLXNFL IEFF EQWEWD XQ JXZEQH YFXQH YQT DABEQH DX NKD DMEQHW

EQ ED."

    — DLAAB NAYDJMLDD

23. "AT AWH RKFM AWIA KQ QAKEE, AWH NWTEH DFKCHSQH QDSSHFMHSQ."

    — EIT ALD

24. E SECRET WITHIN SI PIXKAPI SV UYCKEOI DEP. Y SYXPIEN KWI

TAAJRH KEGTI ECN XLYKDWIN KWI BEC GITK LYKW KWI XIEK GITK!

25. "HLUVU JVU XUBXTU ELB QB WO J ZWVUFHWBO HLJH IBR'Z LJKU

HLBRQLH HLUWV OJDU EBRTZ, YBVH BM, HRVO HLUD VWQLH JQJWOYH."

    — GBLO LBITJOZ, GBRVOJTWYH

26. MQJFAZ RMZYU NRT CNRHA IAVY NZA YUA BMVY ZAQJNLQA XAMXQA YM

NVC PMZ TJZAOYJMRV.

27. "C QXUFGXK QRGJ UJR, GXTXF DR OFXADQX OCDP U MCJ. WRI JXD

KCFDW, UGK YXACKXA, DPX MCJ QCVXA CD."

    — JXRFJX YXFGUFK APUO

Cryptograms - continued

28. "KSH FYJLO'A OJRJLLCESVN TJCO KJAAJE. LGOMVYDJEL CEJO'A KJAAJE

    ABCO PSYVJAL."

    — JFOC MJEKJE

29. "AD RPWVB AD VPWN JK AD RJUOA W MJVP; PSPVE KERRWCRP AOWA

    JK KYPRRPN DFA JK W KYWVZ."

    — SJQADV OFUD

30. "ZUXT CYP VMX TYL GMVKLNKNTO, HYBXYTX XIHX NH OXLLNTO DXLLXM."

    — VIIXT NQXMHYT

31. "TMS HKCCKY DSC COK ZABBV AE LMSY ZAKDKP HKDVSPK A'J EMC

    OSEFYT KEMSFO CM KVC PAU."

    — TMFA HKYYV

32. LXF AMJELJUA CIU CMEKV OKGA. AUU WXM FCGD DXK QCG HKUAA. JE

    DXK HUL ALKQR, CGXLWUI OKTTVU JG LWJA PXXR WCA CVV XE LWU MXIZA.

    "QKOJZ AWXL FU," LXF ACJZ _____.

    "J NXJGUZ LWU GCBD," LXF ACJZ _____.

    "J XGVD ˌAUCAXG FD OXL IXCAL MJLW ACHU CGZ IXAUFCID," LXF

    ACJZ _____.

    "AKU FU," LXF ACJZ _____.

Cryptograms - continued

33. "CTU'S SHWF NUWVRR ETN DHU OGBJTZV SQV ROWVUDV."

    - KTJMV WNOR XTJMVR

34. You'll be seeing red after you've finished this list!

NWKVBPF

XKFE

NIWVKFD

WPBDJPPH

NPWHPSIF

RIWFDA

SDWVKYKPF

BIYVPF

NKFFICIW

BNIWYDA

APVIAP

35. Mr. Watson, come here; I want you. I need a list of telephone styles.

CNQWTL

EAWVKLPP

KNAUTLPP

XWULNEBNVL

HTWE EBNVL

YAWCTWVL

ANYRAS EBNVL

PRYLTTWYL EBNVL

PCRAYEBNVL

WEBNVL

36. Could you walk a mile in these shoes?

VJDHJQV

EQFRV

GVLJHOCQQGV

SGQQCGV

XFEEJVCDV

QFJAGOV

VDGJZGOV

LYXLV

VBCQGBBFV

37. This list is for dog lovers only!

TEYOZ   RCPOEPQ

RETTCZ   NKJOQ

QEANTNJOQ

RJFF   ZCPPYCP

BCDYOUCTC

YPYTN   TCZZCP

MNYBBCZ

UKFQCO   PCZPYCICP

TESKWCQ

QEFSEZYEO

EHUNEO   NKJOQ

UCPSEO   TNCBNCPQ

BJU

FCKORCPUCP

Marching Orders

These puzzles will test your ability to find patterns. In each of the first four rows, fill in the final sequence with the proper letters and/or numbers. On the fifth row, choose the correct continuation (A, B, C or D.)

Answers are on page 131.

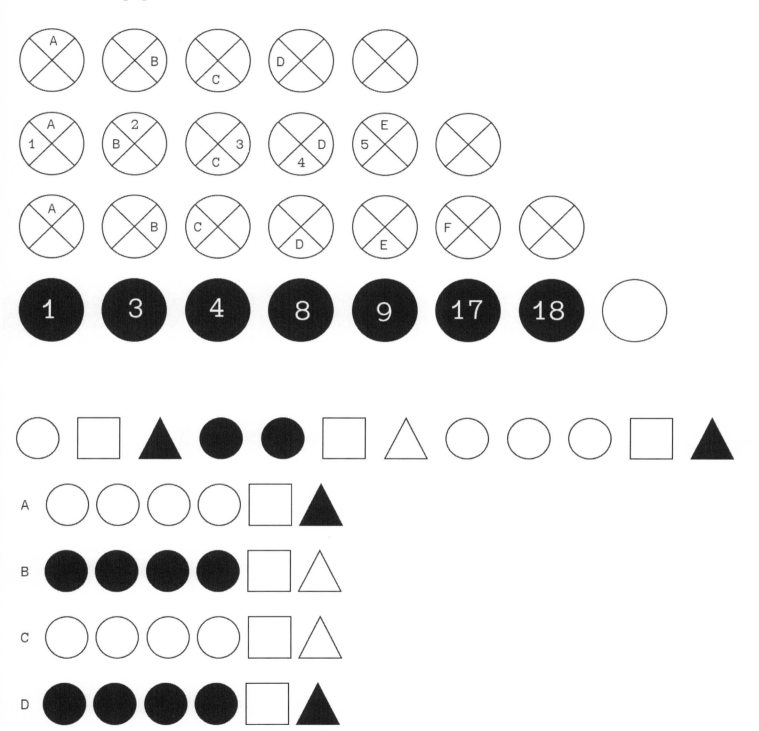

Shrink(age)

Your order of 7-letter words was split into two shipments. The first shipment came last week and you've already assembled the 20-piece rack. The second shipment is in the box.

To complete your project, choose 4 letters by moving from letter to letter in any direction. You may not retrace your path, stay on the same letter, go outside the box or jump over letters. Write each 4-letter group in the spaces provided to form a 7-letter word ending in **AGE**. AVERAGE is done for you.

Answers are on page 131 but you may find more than 20.

M H	O T	S	
U P	M	T S	S E
L B	A	S E	R
T N	O	E V	R P
D L	L	I	M

___AVER___AGE   _____AGE   _____AGE   _____AGE

_____AGE   _____AGE   _____AGE   _____AGE

_____AGE   _____AGE   _____AGE   _____AGE

_____AGE   _____AGE   _____AGE   _____AGE

_____AGE   _____AGE   _____AGE   _____AGE

*Bonus: replace AGE with **ION** and find as many words of seven or more letters as you can, using groups of 4 or more letters from the box. The same movement restrictions apply.*

Out of Order!

Unscramble the letters to find five related words. Use the circled letters to complete the poem. Answers are on page 131.

Things Apartment Dwellers Shouldn't Have to Worry About

HAET

TEARW

KSINOGM

ITIETYLCRCE

TERROFARIERG

Upstairs neighbor, with two young boys,

Constant stomping and lots of noise.

Glenda Good Witch tries appealing

By using broom, she ○○○○○○ ○○○○○○ .

Chuck Wagon

Unscramble the letters to find six related words. Use the circled letters to complete the quip. Answers are on page 131.

Food from the Chuck wagon

WSET

SHIF

EABNS

EGRUBRS

SDOTOGH

OTAABKTEODP

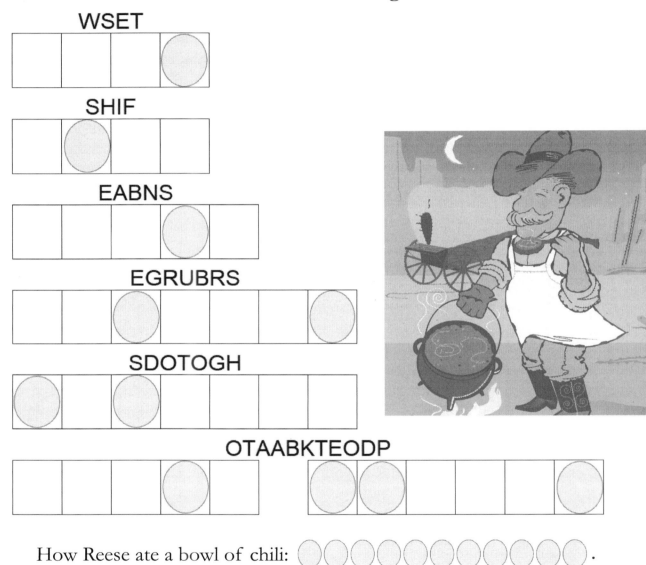

How Reese ate a bowl of chili: ○○○○○○○○○○○ .

Arboretum

Unscramble the letters to find four related words. Use the circled letters to complete the quip. Answers are on page 131.

A List of Trees

ATKE

BCRIH

DDWOOOG

MASCROYE

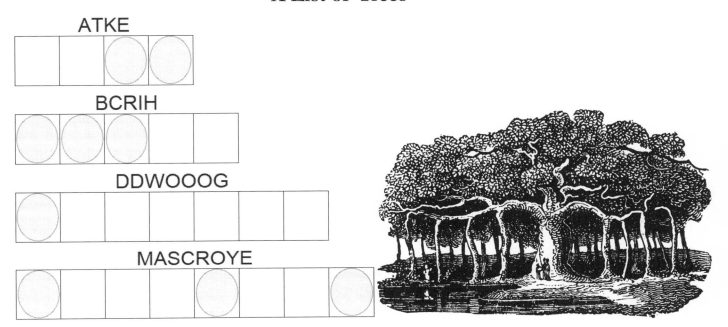

How trees leave a cruise ship: they ◯◯◯◯◯◯◯◯◯ .

Rich Man, Poor Man

Tinker, tailor

Soldier, sailor

Rich man, poor man

Beggarman, thief.

In this vocabulary challenge, you are to place each of the synonyms on the proper row. (A synonym is a word that means the same as another word. For example, **robber** is a synonym for thief.)

Just for fun, some of the synonyms are archaic. To help you out, each main word has three synonyms.

Answers are on page 131.

Tinker			
Tailor			
Soldier			
Sailor			
Rich man			
Poor man			
Beggarman			
Thief			

affluent bandit bankrupt bricoleur
condottiere couturier cutpurse destitute
dogface   doughboy
factotum   guttersnipe
handyman   jacktar
leatherneck   millionaire
modiste   palliard
penurious   prosperous
purloiner sartor shellback spanger

Alphabet Soup

Don't cry over spilled soup! For each group of pasta letters, can you think of the shortest word that contains **all** of those letters, in some order? Four of the spoons have a single answer, one spoon has two answers and one spoon has 14! Proper nouns and hyphenated words are not allowed.

The answers, on page 131, include common and uncommon words.

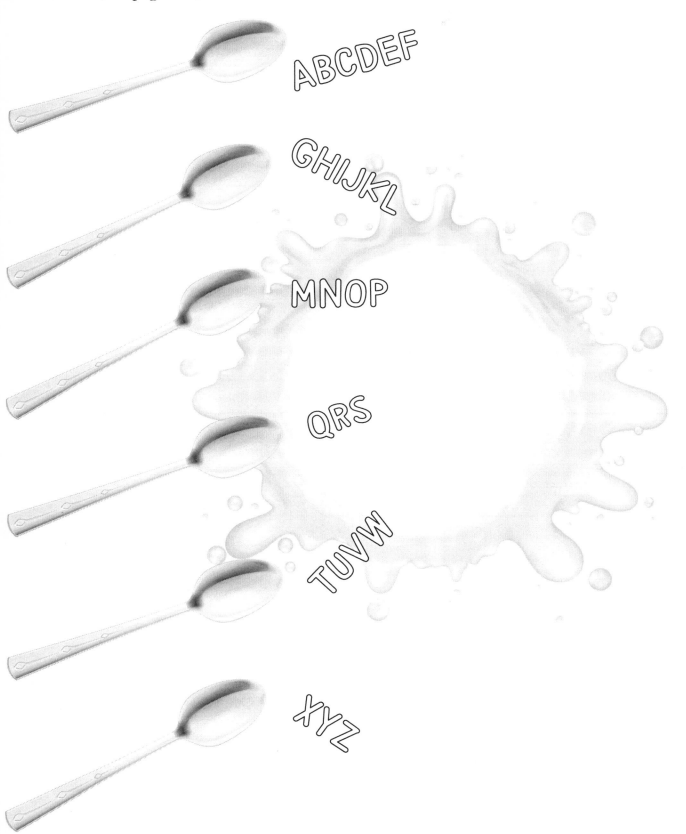

Poetic PUN-ishment

Solage is a specific form of humorous verse that consists of three lines of irregular length. The rhyming structure is **AAB**. The third line is a pun based on the previous two lines. Here is an example:

Literary Arpeggio
Chords' marching genesis, playfully penned.
Exalted exodus - three sheets to the wind.

Grand opening sail.

Test your composition skills by picking from the group of words in the box to complete the following poems. The blanks indicate how many words are needed. When you are done, the unused words, arranged alphabetically, describe another poetry form.

Answers are on page 131.

Happy Birthday
Seven years since those terrible twos,
We celebrate the path you choose -

_____.

Stars In Your Eyes?
The quality of night vision depends
On the grind of the optical lens:

_____ _____.

Chasing Puck
As they skid to a stop with a slice
From their skates comes a fine spray of ice:

_____ of the _____.

Risqué Business
Erasing the ignominy of impotence,
The blue pill resurrected his wooden fence,

Until he was _____ _____.

Secretary Estate
As a matter of national security
She lived rent-free in obscurity.

_____ _____ _____.

Soft Shoulder
Take a look back at Lot's marital life.
Picture them playing: he tickles his wife;

She _____ to a _____ _____.

WITTY   RINKS
THAT'S   ARISE
LINES   CRUDE
FIVE   BENIGN
MAKE   INSERTION
PILLOW   STANZA
CONDO   STIFF
TURNS   BLATANTLY
DITTY   BOARD
ONE   EXACTLY
ORBITAL   ASSAULT
LEASE   SPITTLE
A

Rock, Paper, Scissors, BOOM!

Can you navigate these treacherous mazes? Start at any outstretched hand. Move north, south, east or west to an adjacent space. Watch out for bombs!

Movement

- You must never land next to a bomb *unless* you land on a pair of scissors. All eight spaces adjacent to a bomb (those without a pair of scissors) are to avoided!
- you can only move **from** a rock **to** a pair of scissors or a hand
- you can only move **from** a pair of scissors **to** a sheet of paper or a hand
- you can only move **from** a sheet of paper **to** a rock or a hand
- You can move from a **pointing** hand only in the direction it is pointing, unless it points to a bomb
- You can move from an **outstretched** hand north, south, east or west to rock, paper, scissors or another hand
- Try to reach the hand that points outside of the maze

Defusing a Bomb

If you land on a pair of scissors that happens to be adjacent to a bomb (even diagonally), you automatically defuse it. Place an "X" on the bomb. This removes the restriction on landing next to that bomb. You still are not allowed to land on a defused bomb.

Check out the example. The highlighted path is the only way out. The bomb prevents you from jumping from the hand just above it to south or west. Going north, then being forced west to land on the paper is a dead-end. Going east defuses the bomb, but you still are forced to proceed north and west to the dead-end. The southernmost outstretched hand also dead ends. Therefore, you must start on the highlighted hand.

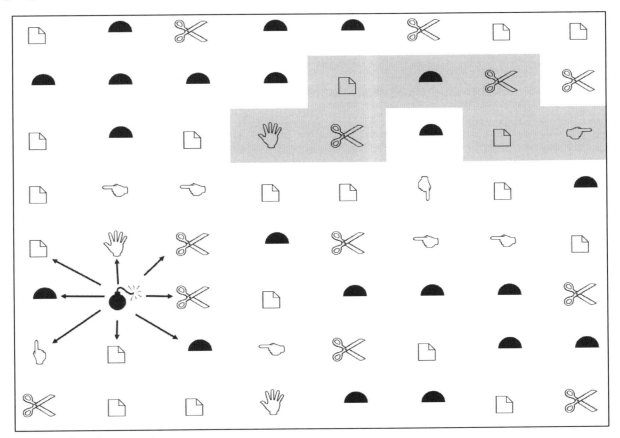

Turn the page to begin your journey.

Rock, Paper, Scissors, BOOM! #1

Start from any outstretched hand. Beware the bomb.

Answer is on page 131.

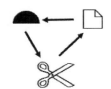

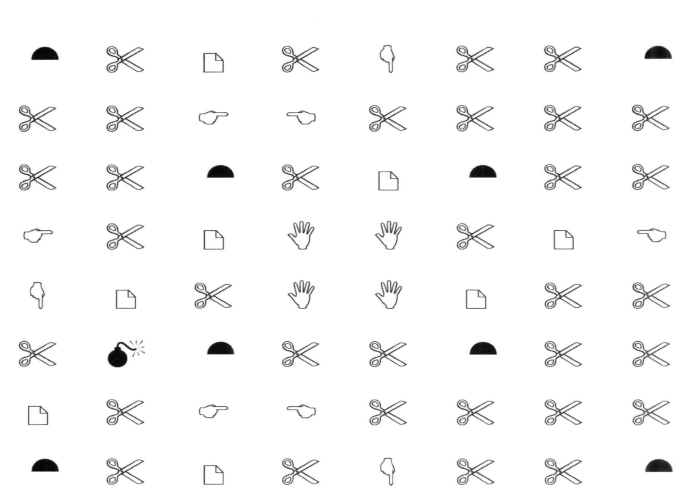

Rock, Paper, Scissors, BOOM! #2

Start from the outstretched hand. The bomb allows you to proceed in one direction only. Thankfully, you land on a pair of scissors. Snip that fuse and continue on your way!

Answer is on page 131.

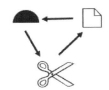

Elements of Style

You've been invited to tour the Cricket City Chemical Couture Company. The lead scientist, a designer who has created award-winning fashionable clothes, gives you a pair of goggles, some beakers and a chance to mix chemicals to make some basic clothes and accessories.

Use any combination of symbols from the table, to make whatever you'd like. For example, **H At** or **S O C K S**. (You may want to use a blank sheet of paper, if you're feeling creative.)

29 humble designs appear on page 132.

H																	He
Li	Be											B	C	N	O	F	Ne
Na	Mg											Al	Si	P	S	Cl	Ar
K	Ca	Sc	Ti	V	Cr	Mn	Fe	Co	Ni	Cu	Zn	Ga	Ge	As	Se	Br	Kr
Rb	Sr	Y	Zr	Nb	Mo	Tc	Ru	Rh	Pd	Ag	Cd	In	Sn	Sb	Te	I	Xe
Cs	Ba	La	Hf	Ta	W	Re	Os	Ir	Pt	Au	Hg	Tl	Pb	Bi	Po	At	Rn
Fr	Ra	Ac	Rf	Db	Sg	Bh	Hs	Mt	Ds	Rg	Cn	Nh	Fl	Mc	Lv	Ts	Og

			Ce	Pr	Nd	Pm	Sm	Eu	Gd	Tb	Dy	Ho	Er	Tm	Yb	Lu
			Th	Pa	U	Np	Pu	Am	Cm	Bk	Cf	Es	Fm	Md	No	Lr

Here is an alphabetical list:

Ac	Ag	Al	Am	Ar	As	At	Au	B	Ba	Be	Bh	Bi	Bk	Br
C	Ca	Cd	Ce	Cf	Cl	Cm	Cn	Co	Cr	Cs	Cu	Db	Ds	Dy
Er	Es	Eu	F	Fe	Fl	Fm	Fr	Ga	Gd	Ge	H	He	Hf	Hg
Ho	Hs	I	In	Ir	K	Kr	La	Li	Lr	Lu	Lv	Mc	Md	Mg
Mn	Mo	Mt	N	Na	Nb	Nd	Ne	Nh	Ni	No	Np	O	Og	Os
P	Pa	Pb	Pd	Pm	Po	Pr	Pt	Pu	Ra	Rb	Re	Rf	Rg	Rh
Rn	Ru	S	Sb	Sc	Se	Sg	Si	Sm	Sn	Sr	Ta	Tb	Tc	Te
Th	Ti	Tl	Tm	Ts	U	V	W	Xe	Y	Yb	Zn	Zr		

Pyramid Scheme

The Cricket City Conspiracy Club has uncovered what it thinks is a sinister message from industries that seek to control decisions we make about our bodies. Members claim that, by copying a vertical strip from each of the five blocks, a sixth block can be constructed with a hidden message that reads from top to bottom.

Choose a strip from column 1 of any block. Copy its letters into one of the empty columns of the answer block. Repeat for columns 2-5. If you select the right columns *and* choose the proper empty column for each, the "conspiracy" will be revealed.

Answer is on page 132.

1	2	3	4	5

1	2	3	4	5
V	E	G	A	N
S	H	A	N	K
T	H	I	G	H
R	O	U	N	D
Q	U	A	I	L

1	2	3	4	5
H	A	L	V	A
S	W	E	E	T
C	I	D	E	R
M	O	C	H	I
D	O	L	C	I

1	2	3	4	5
P	O	O	R	I
G	R	I	S	T
S	H	O	Y	U
M	U	L	T	I
B	R	A	N	S

1	2	3	4	5
G	U	A	V	A
L	E	M	O	N
M	A	N	G	O
P	R	U	N	E
G	R	A	P	E

1	2	3	4	5
S	W	I	S	S
M	I	L	C	H
D	E	F	A	T
F	L	O	A	T
G	O	U	D	A

A.W.O.L.

Eight letters have gone missing! A single letter is needed for completing one row of six words. For example, **Z** could be added to EBRA, LAY, CAR, FROE, WALT and BOO to form ZEBRA, LAZY, CZAR, FROZE, WALTZ and BOZO.

If you find the correct letters and write them on the blanks provided, you will discover a related word reading from top to bottom. You may use the same letter on more than one row.

It is possible to choose letters other than those that form the related word.

Answer is on page 132.

____	ABOE	COE	AUNT	IVA	LAING	GRAES
____	BLLY	GRM	CHCK	HOMLY	MLD	WLT
____	BAING	DAIY	INET	AVAGE	PATED	WHOE
____	GUNMN	HCK	MLLOW	PRSON	FLUNT	DRW
____	DAM	SCOE	COVE	DOZE	UTS	PATIES
____	WHIE	BUS	HUCH	MEA	SPIE	CRAE
____	MSSY	OUTLT	OYSTR	PBBLY	CLOTH	TNTH
____	DEVOU	CLEA	OOK	EASE	HAES	MACH

Punagrams

When a pun and an anagram have a party, they always drink too much. However, instead of slurring their words, they just mix them up.

If you want to get in on the joke, you have to decipher it yourself. The pun is always on the left and the anagram is on the right. Hopefully, the image will give you a clue. For example, the first image shows a boxer. What does a boxer have to do with hairstyles? Just play with the letters (hint, three words, second word is **AND**.)

Answers are on page 132.

Boxer's hairstyles?   BE ABOVE DAWN

Sunburnt Red Sox fan?   KNOBBIEST BONDAGE

Babe Ruth's macaroni art?   ONE LOADED KEY

Best time to obtain pork sausages!   HUNGRY? ADD GOO

Take your date to a treehouse?

UM, OBLATION

Knead, roll, fill, bake, cool, eat

FLEE IF POI

League of Bad Bowlers

Cricket City is world-famous for its annual bowling tournament. In its 25-year history, no participant has ever managed to knock down all ten pins in a single frame. To celebrate this dubious record, you can join the league or, for a tougher challenge try to snap the streak!

Three frames are set up, below. You get two rolls per frame. A pin can only be used in one word, so "knock down" the pins whose letters make up that word by crossing them out.

If you find a five-letter word and a four-letter word for each frame, the League will welcome you with open arms. If you find even one ten-letter word, you'll be banned from membership, but at least you'll know you're not a bad bowler! Find all three ten-letter words for a turkey trophy.

Word lists are on page 132.

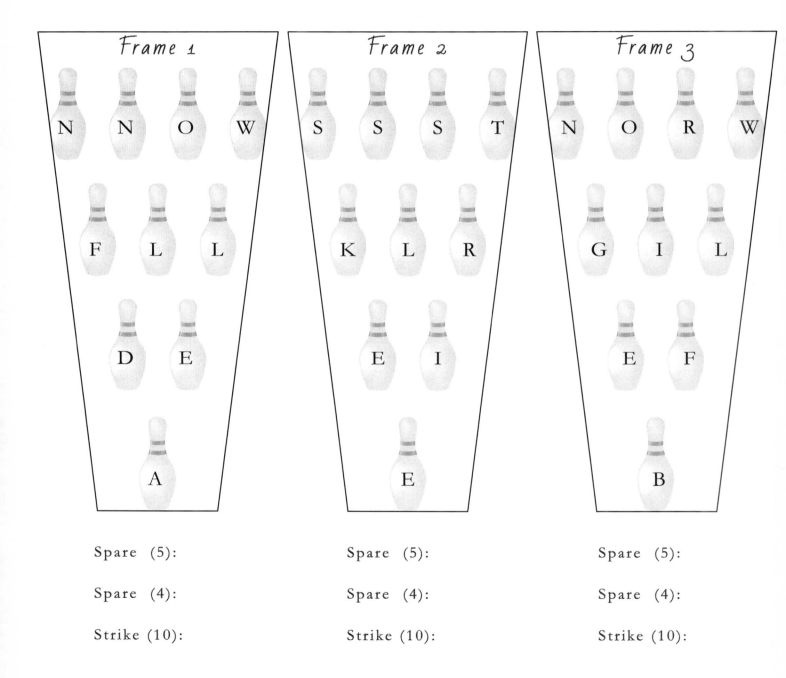

Frame 1	Frame 2	Frame 3
N N O W	S S S T	N O R W
F L L	K L R	G I L
D E	E I	E F
A	E	B

Spare (5):   Spare (5):   Spare (5):

Spare (4):   Spare (4):   Spare (4):

Strike (10):   Strike (10):   Strike (10):

I.O.U.

Old MacDonald had a farm. He borrowed all the vowels from his vegetable patch for seed money. The vegetables have issued demand letters, so the poor farmer needs your help to return the I's O's and U's to them. Cross out each letter as you fill in the blanks.

Answers are on page 132.

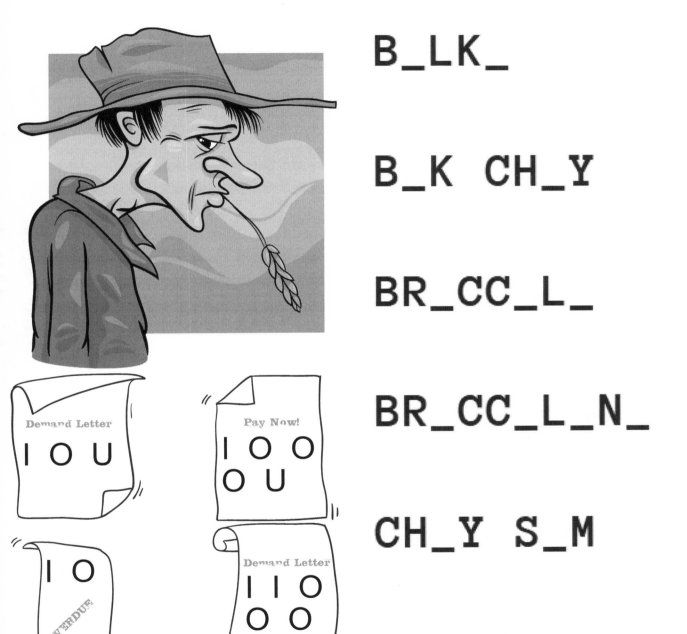

B_LK_

B_K CH_Y

BR_CC_L_

BR_CC_L_N_

CH_Y S_M

R_B_C_N

Conga Words

Build a "conga line" of words by appending letters to the end of the previous word suggested by the clue. Each answer shares one or more letters with its neighbors, but one answer will never contain all of another answer.

For example, given the clues *whine*, *doorway* and *one-night stand*, your answers might be LAMENT, ENTRY and TRYST. (if it helps, you may write one long string of letters: LAMENTRYST.)

One possible answer is on page 132.

1. Skipjack, e.g.
2. Related to the nose
3. Type of bar
4. Used for climbing
5. Horse race
6. Eight bits
7. Lukewarm
8. Live in
9. Oval
10. Moniker
11. Dryad or maenad
12. Verbal
13. Stroke lightly
14. Recurrent urge to steal
15. Shakespeare's meter
16. Two-hundredth anniversary
17. Lightly tinted gypsum
18. Ceres, in space
19. Concept
20. Three-legged frame

1.	
2.	
3.	
4.	
5.	
6.	
7.	
8.	
9.	
10.	
11.	
12.	
13.	
14.	
15.	
16.	
17.	
18.	
19.	
20.	

Navy Beans

In this puzzle, you have to sink a fleet of ten warships. Each warship has 2-6 letters of armor plating. You have to fire different types of beans at the fleet. Each letter in a bean scores a hit if you can cross off a letter on one of the ships. Otherwise, the letter is a miss. When all letters on a ship have been crossed off, that ship sinks. If you miss three times, the fleet escapes.

You can use any legume; however, if the name contains BEAN, you may not use those four letters. For example, with NAVY BEAN, you only have four shots, not eight. Finally, you may use a specific bean only once.

Perfect salvos are on page 132.

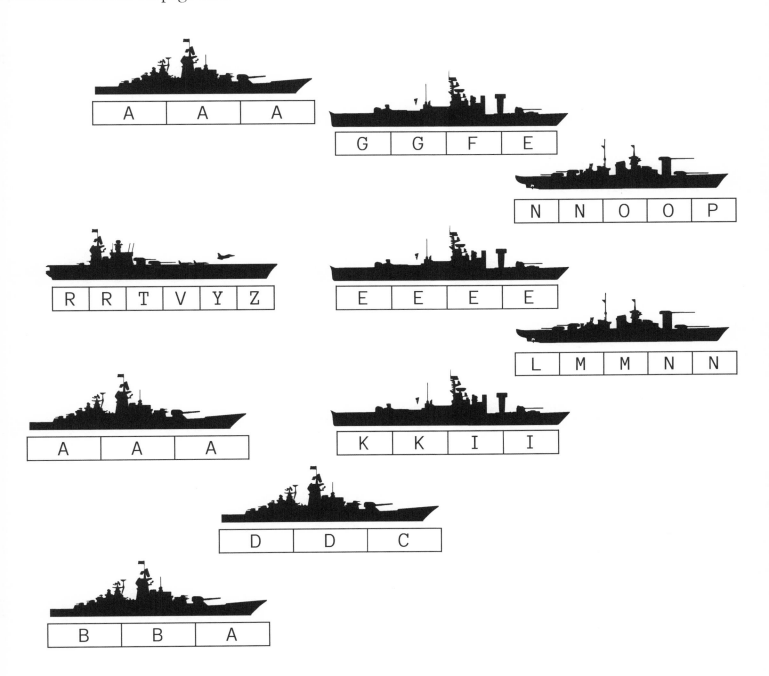

Engine Engine #9

Johnny likes to crash trains on his model railroad. He clears the tracks so that the next crash can occur. The trains depart at different times, run at different speeds and either arrive safely or crash en route.

The two schedules show departure times and speeds of each train. Can you figure out which two trains collided at the location shown below? Since these are model trains, they reach top speed instantly.

Answer and explanation are on page 133.

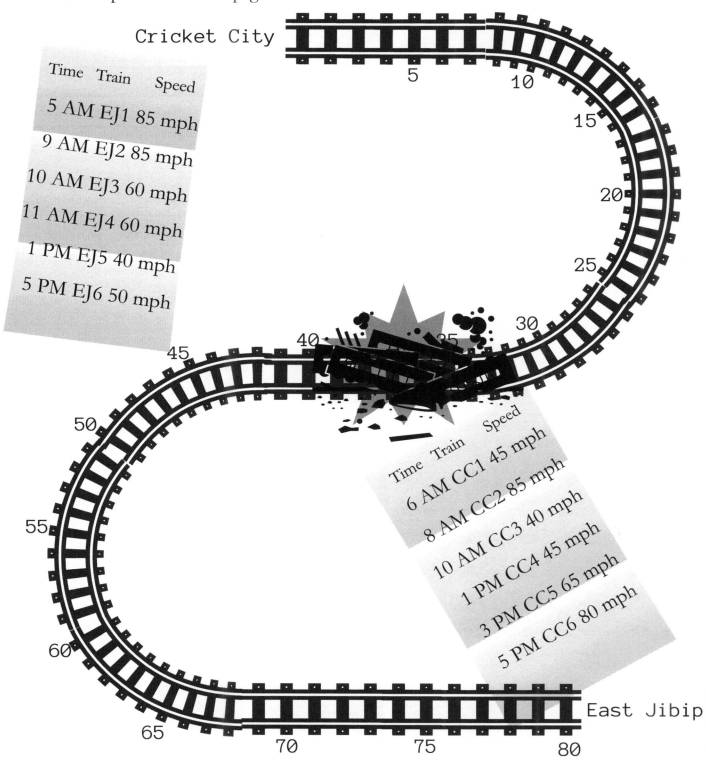

Cricket City

Time	Train	Speed
5 AM	EJ1	85 mph
9 AM	EJ2	85 mph
10 AM	EJ3	60 mph
11 AM	EJ4	60 mph
1 PM	EJ5	40 mph
5 PM	EJ6	50 mph

Time	Train	Speed
6 AM	CC1	45 mph
8 AM	CC2	85 mph
10 AM	CC3	40 mph
1 PM	CC4	45 mph
3 PM	CC5	65 mph
5 PM	CC6	80 mph

East Jibip

Pepper Pop Quiz

Can you identify these references?
Answers are on page 133.

1. Lucy in the Sky with Diamonds

2. Pizza

3. Flea

4. Marcie's best friend

5. Angie Dickinson

6. Tongue-twister

7. Former NFL defensive end

8. Tony Stark

9. Carolina Reaper's parents

10. Charles Alderton

Window Shopping

How well do you know windows? Cross out any term that has nothing to do with windows.
Answers are on page 133.

Bay   Dingus   Oriel
Bichon Frise   French   Portico
Casement   Guillotine   Stained-glass
Clerestory   Jalousie   Transom
Corbel   Lancet   Witch

What Entitles These People?

Can you figure out what's going on here? Use your trivia super power or use Google. If all else fails, the answers are on page 133. (For a hint, turn the page upside down.)

Clue	Name	Rank	Serial#
Father and Restorer of Letters			
The Steward			
White Rose Loser			
House of Hanover			
Crushed by Solway Moss Defeat			
From "the Beloved" to "the Mad"			
Bertie			
Device Forts			
Eighth Crusade Loser			

Nine other puzzles in this book will help you complete the **Name** column.

What the Hex?

"It's LeviOsa, not LeviosA" - Hermione Granger

Hexes in these puzzles are completely mixed up and your homework is to figure out the correct incantation. An incantation may invoke a saying, phrase or a simple list that is spoken in a specific order.

Each grid has several connected groups of letters. One letter in each group has been replaced by a "?". Below the grid is your spellbook, with an enchantment. Use each letter of the enchantment for one of the missing letters. When you correctly replace each missing letter, you will be able to rearrange the letters in each group to form a word. Only use each enchantment letter once.

To get full credit, rearrange the letters in your spellbook into incantation order. Here is a simple example, where the grid letters are **not** scrambled:

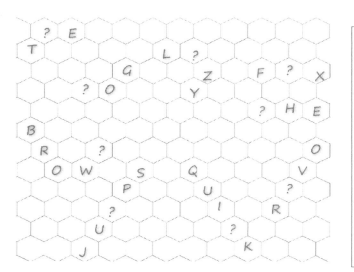

Reading from left to right and top to bottom:

T?E ?OG L?ZYF?X ?HE BROW? JU?PS QUI?K OV?R

becomes:

THE DOG LAZY FOX THE BROWN JUMPS QUICK OVER

which just might remind you of:

THE QUICK BROWN FOX JUMPS OVER THE LAZY DOG

The enchanted letters, in order of this incantation, are rearranged as shown. Since "THE" appeared twice in the grid, either rearrangement is acceptable.

Remember, the grid letters will be scrambled, unlike this example. The answers are on page 133.

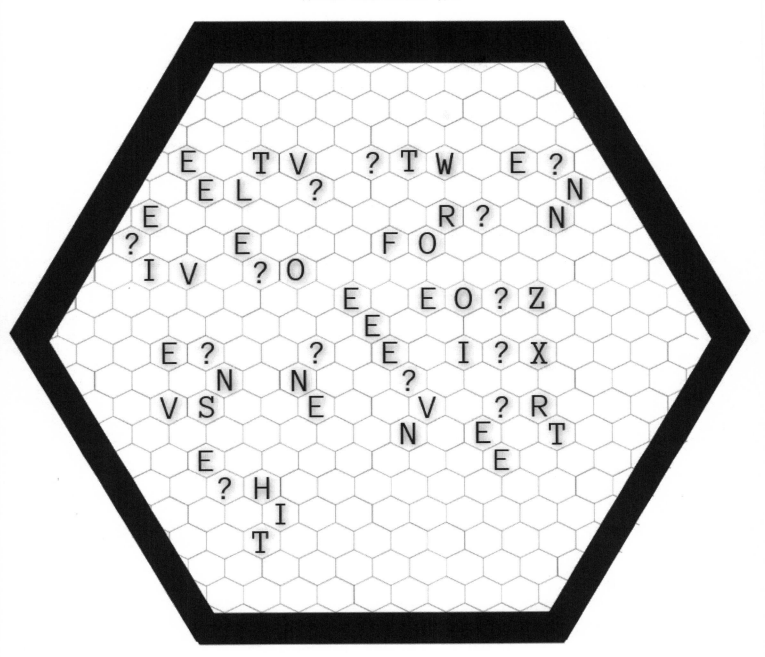

WHISTLE FOG RUN

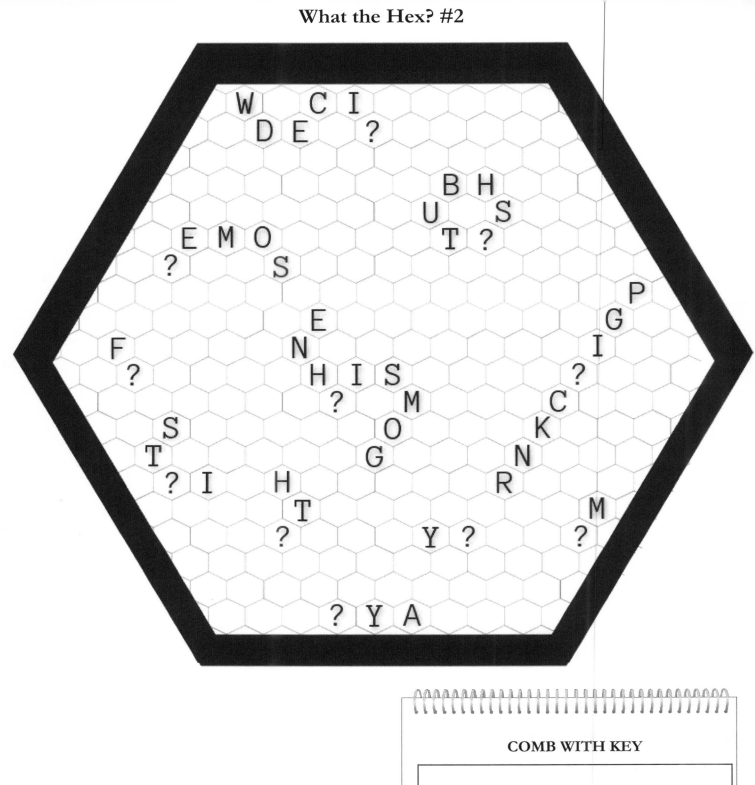

COMB WITH KEY

What the Hex? #3

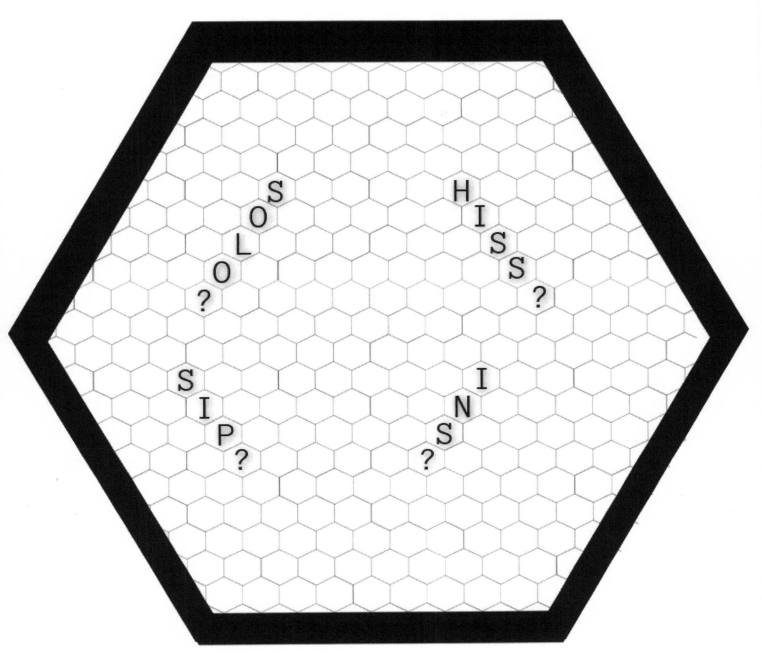

KELP

Eight is Not Enough

In the grid below, try to find three 9-letter words by moving from letter to letter in any direction. You may not retrace your path, stay on the same letter, go outside the grid or jump over letters. For a couple of hints, turn this page upside-down.

Answers are on page 133.

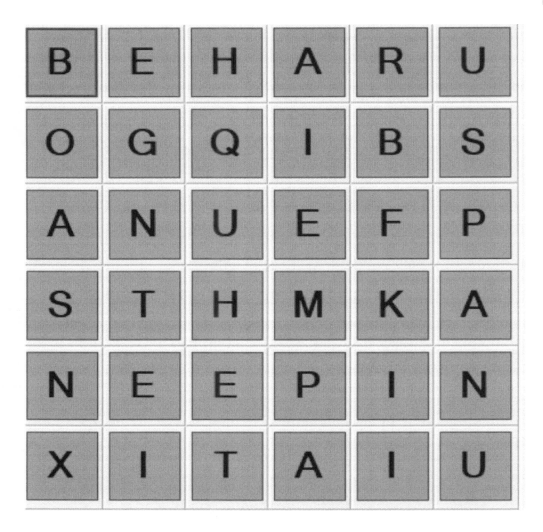

1.

2.

3.

Each word begins with a vowel. Five particular blocks appear in all three words.

3 x 5 = 15

Each of the four puzzles below has five 3-letter words, which are to be rearranged into three, loosely related 5-letter words and one 15-letter word suggested by the title and image.

To help you focus, the initial letter is given for each 5-letter word.

Answers are on page 133.

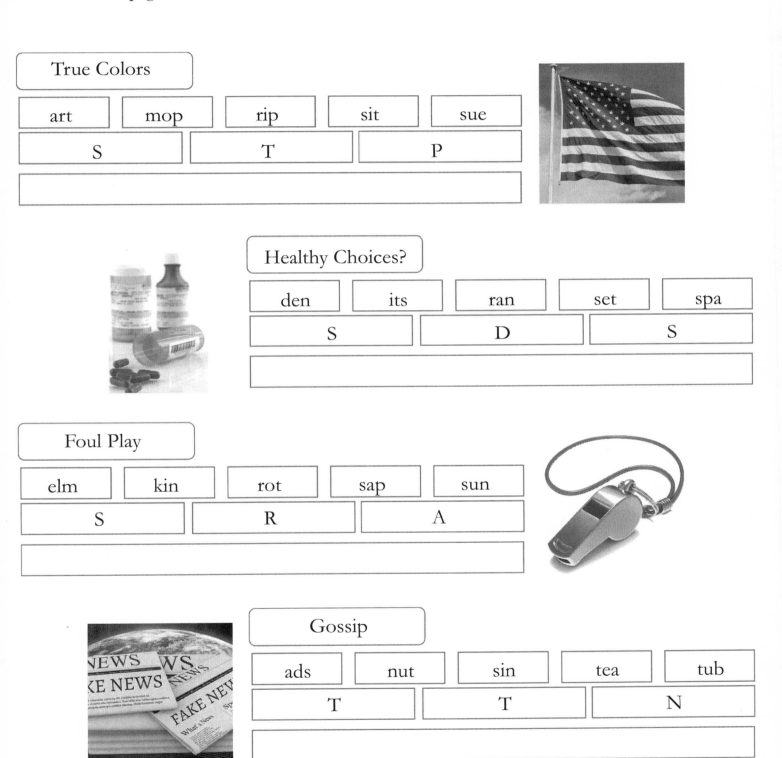

True Colors

| art | mop | rip | sit | sue |

| S | T | P |

Healthy Choices?

| den | its | ran | set | spa |

| S | D | S |

Foul Play

| elm | kin | rot | sap | sun |

| S | R | A |

Gossip

| ads | nut | sin | tea | tub |

| T | T | N |

Dollar Bill Y'All

"A little stash of the cash put aside in a safe." - Erik Schrody

Can you match the currency on the left with the country on the right? You can solve this in one of three ways: through your sheer knowledge of trivia; by looking for a specific connection between the words on the left and the words on the right; or, by completing the logic puzzle.

Some currency is no longer in use.

Answers are on page 133.

baht	Angola
dirham	Cameroon
ekwele	Ecuador
franc	Equatorial Guinea
gulden	Morocco
kwanza	Netherlands
manat	Thailand
sucre	Turkmenistan

1. Four of the matches involve franc, kwanza, Morocco and Thailand.
2. If Turkmenistan matches sucre, then Ecuador matches ekwele; otherwise, Thailand matches baht.
3. Franc matches either Cameroon or Morocco.
4. Only one match has the same initials.
5. Ecuador and Turkmenistan match manat and sucre in some order.
6. Angola, Morocco and Thailand match baht, dirham and kwanza in some order.

Decisions, Decisions

At the Cricket City Letter Bank, you can only withdraw ten letters at a time. However, on any given visit, only four different letters are available! To ensure that each customer has access to all of the letters, the teller will distribute them as follows: one of one letter, two of a different letter, three of another different letter and four of the remaining letter. This isn't too bad, as you get to decide which letters you need most.

For example, if the letters were **ABCD**, you'd withdraw AAAA BBB CC D or DDDD AAA BB C or any of the other possible combinations.

You have to make two trips to the bank, for two completely different tasks, listed below. Each teller shows you what letters are available during each trip. Can you withdraw the right amount of of each letter to complete each task?

Answers are on page 133.

Create a ten-letter word, using P E R T

Create two five-letter words, using A L M S

To Be Frank

Can you find a dozen words that, when paired, form six synonyms for FRANK? For example, GUILE + LESS can be paired to form GUILELESS.

To assist you, 12 clues are given for the words chosen as the solution. Write your answers on the proper numbered lines in the speech bubbles.

Answers are on page 133.

1. Able to

2. Awake

3. Carried out

4. Correct

5. Embark

6. Higher Up

7. Into view

8. Not crooked

9. Not present

10. Obverse

11. Presumptuous

12. Voiced

I'm Steamed Up

A classic Word Search puzzle contains related words that are hidden in a grid. The words are always in a straight line, but may read forward, backward, horizontally, vertically or diagonally. If the puzzle has special instructions, be sure to read them carefully.

Answer is on page 134.

```
N C M D I W S R Y B A D B O E I G V A V L W V H U
G C S H Y K W N V M I L W V U G Z X V L W O H Y A
N O N E P A L A J V I W J J N S V T I L T R W S L
M D N B L Z Y K I S W A M I D J V R Y E T S A F I
Y A W V S I Q L T A E M H V P G G R M L Q U W T X
T W G M P H R E E I D T V G V K V E M W N O L I H
X E H I O C R P B E E A N X G V Y L G A E I Y H D
V X C T N I C U G E R I L R H M Y L J Z C R R R P
N P T G N V T A S L D J S E Q K Z O W X N U Q D Y
K U V G F T R I O L Q G S V L S K R Q F V F W K V
B D S H Z T M E A V I B M E M Z T M S Z E O I T P
U G C C U N E C L S J T M F D D U A Q T H L S J U
H R S O F O S O U J K A L P A V C E W M K D J B E
P U N S C R U R O O F V Q R J H Z T V I S F Q Y C
R U S U C D Z I Q M Q A R T F Q K S Z Z A A J B A
E Y C I X L E B Y E L L A V H T A E D N G I D Q L
P L E F V U V V Q B T F V B M O U E G X F T T K P
P S C G M A H H L X U O V O X P D R H I H H S R E
J Q F E A C Z Q Z D B I U N M A Y R F K P F P M R
B X Y O S P D D F H H C B U Q E E J R U R U Z Q I
G J E P W Q M B G N S Y W U X T V M V V R L E Y F
S L T P P R V A B G D F U A L Q P L P N D N C H E
U X X U M T E S R C X L Z E H H G M L K O C A A Q
L T S H I E X O T H E R M I C M W X C T Z E L C I
X K C A F E F P R W P S S U M M E R A D A B V O E
```

Angry	Fireplace	Lava	Sauna	Sun
Blistering	Furious	Livid	Scalding	Teapot
Cauldron	Furnace	Old	Seething	Wrath
Death Valley	Grill	Faithful	Smelter	
Exothermic	Hot tub	Outraged	Steamroller	
Fever	Jalapeno	Rampage	Summer	

Driver's Ed

Find the driving-related terms in this puzzle.
Answer is on page 134.

```
S P Z F P W N Z T D X L E P D J K F J C S
T B R K M G F J R F L H F E E B X S A W B
C L G O I S V P A H S Z E L R F K D M D S
N T S S U T Z N F C S P N N Y R G W E B X
P F N Y Z N P T F R S F K R O A V O R T H
A C G Y A F D V I A A L D U K R L R G S I
V X D E C N P A C E A M I J A M F K E R G
E J N E E K I X B W B S P A R K V Z T N H
M C M A D I S K S O E R K C A P L O U J W
E P G E M I T S T Z U Q A N C B N N N X A
N E G G I Q O P V L B T U K N B M E N O Y
T D L G P R P T A I L G A T E P Y I E F T
U E R E C N K A B X M S L Q T C H U L H I
V S C N H Z M V E V I P D Y I W J Q C H F
X T O I A S Q Y I E L D P N I D N H B V A
X R N S M Q I E E J E I Y A D G E D H E H
M I R R O R D A I X L E N I S L E T V G F
J A C M K J T K K M U U C H L S O R O M K
B N X F R O A D V E H I C L E W U C U U I
E D K W Y N S K I D R F T J Q C I Q Z U R
L U L T Z Q F M W C F H B U Z S P M Q N Q
```

Brake	Pass	Speed
Crosswalk	Pavement	Stop
Curve	Pedestrian	Tailgate
Detour	Ramp	Traffic
Highway	Road	Tunnel
Merge	Roundabout	Vehicle
Mirror	Sign	Work zone
Park	Skid	Yield

Double Trouble

In this word search, locate 17 words with doubled letters. The initial letter of each word is given below.

Answer is on page 134.

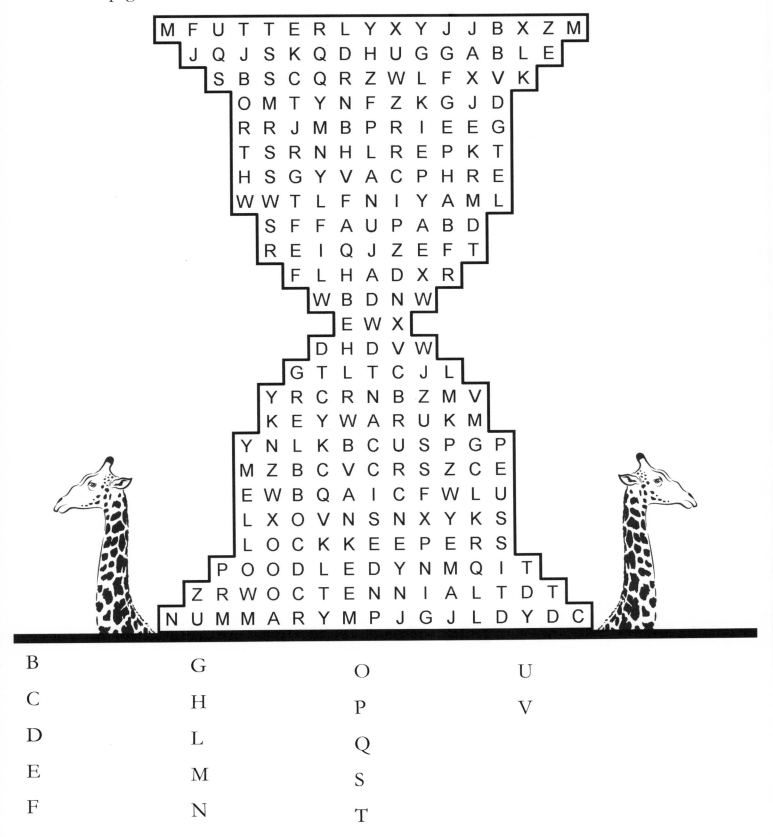

M F U T T E R L Y X Y J J B X Z M
J Q J S K Q D H U G G A B L E
S B S C Q R Z W L F X V K
O M T Y N F Z K G J D
R R J M B P R I E E G
T S R N H L R E P K T
H S G Y V A C P H R E
W W T L F N I Y A M L
S F F A U P A B D
R E I Q J Z E F T
F L H A D X R
W B D N W
E W X
D H D V W
G T L T C J L
Y R C R N B Z M V
K E Y W A R U K M
Y N L K B C U S P G P
M Z B C V C R S Z C E
E W B Q A I C F W L U
L X O V N S N X Y K S
L O C K K E E P E R S
P O O D L E D Y N M Q I T
Z R W O C T E N N I A L T D T
N U M M A R Y M P J G J L D Y D C

B   G   O   U

C   H   P   V

D   L   Q

E   M   S

F   N   T

That's So Meta

This is a word search about words related to searching for words.
Answer is on page 134.

```
D U A E R U T A L C N E M O N N S I O T A P R Z B
I R E W V P Y H P A R G O H T R O Y X T H M L T C
A P Q A C O L G J Y K T D D U K X C V T C U S T F
L Q M F B K B H V L X I D I O M L C I P H T T C G
E M V I O Y B K F I H E E V M V B F M X K H M D O
C S O A D L G R U E O M Y P A F R G T V E N R V U
T I T X G E Y O A Z B A X L R E D D W U G L S A O
T G W S W L U P L L K R N P Q I Z Q L J I E Y I
E O Q N Z C Y K H O U G U F L X D P O B V T W X A
E L J Y N G D G R G M C R J O C L S D L N Y A C M
L O L N E K E P X X S Y A H C P S S P A C F N O M
B E F O H J Q D N K A L T N L A J E M V G F R C E
B N F J T O O Y A R I F E E R F X T U O G X O D L
A F G T F Z Y V M K V L T Y B E R F A E U P D O O
B X Y R A L U B A C O V S X F O V W A L I P G T T
O V L E E O R E K V I C J G P V U N V V K N F E Q
H M D G N O U L H O U M N O G R A J F V I S H Z I
C U H L V Q J M E U B J P M T I O G M L G E H Z V
Y Q F Y D A Y F F K O O G E D E L B B O G M I L C
S Y D I C T I O N A R Y M J B T C A G R O A X K I
P L D I W Y M D P W A D C H S G X Q F N Q N B T H
T F A S B F I V H W S O N C K Z D P K Q U T C M R
E S Y N O N Y M I Q L O O K U P I N D E X I O B L
H P D T G O S P I O D K D G X D S S I B W C D A B
C X H F Q T Y S U R U A S E H T J K T R R S M C Q
```

Dialect	Lemma	Portmanteau
Dictionary	Lexicon	Psychobabble
Etymology	Lingo	Semantics
Glossary	Look Up	Slang
Gobbledegook	Neologism	Synonym
Idiom	Nomenclature	Thesaurus
Index	Orthography	Vernacular
Jargon	Patois	Vocabulary

Coin Collection

In this word search, you're looking for loose change which might be worth a pretty penny.
Answer is on page 135.

```
Y Q L F Z E G Q F P E M E V R Z L V Y Q G N V P I
K K R E U T Z E R R D J B I U L E N W S H S I Q H
W F X T A C U D R L O O N I E J A Q A G W Q W C F
Z N B A V D M F L T R Z I K N J H Y U E K F G I A
L V K W S H K G Z K Q F Y P Y M T O R A S Q E S F
K O B G K Z K S M C K Q Y U A G E I N J R N W C R
C Z R F N B K I O G G E Q A Q H U Q O W X T N S Q
O G G C E N T A V O F O Z S J R L V Q Z U D E F Z
N Q R Q O D B V O J R T M Y A R V A U Y O N S R E
R L O J X P N K T P Q I V N S R M G V B Q E E X P
E Z A B E Z A N T V V A D N V T P N S I J E S O G
V W T U B S I H H N E C N E P P U T O U D R T Y O
I H N B R U H O M Z X K T P Y O S M T O G A E B G
U H C Q D Y V I Q A N I R O L F Z E E J T T R V M
T K S V P S Y V R T F P K N H Y G G M R L S C K E
S M A R A V E D I N B J J U D I N E R O O I E N U
P C O I W B Z F W S I K M J N I K J A J P P U T A
J T A A M R A M H T X C W H L R Z U V X X Y Q R G
P L X U T V B N K V C Y K L B K E J M F A T N X K
E Y U K D P E Q E W A D I E T W F S H C U B K B B
Y J C D B N M V J N P K S U L N I N I U C G I J C
A X K V L A M H A I S A E L O D S P U W T J I E Z
F D O B L A M J Q T P N F S M I R T X S H B X O L
E E I O H R C G U Y M B M C T M I H P Z W J U E X
K M Y J E E D J T U P A Z H T E L Z E I K E O F I
```

Bezant	Groat	Picayune	Testoon
Centavo	Kreutzer	Pistareen	Tuppence
Dime	Loonie	Quarter	
Dinero	Maravedi	Ryal	
Dobla	Mohur	Sesterce	
Ducat	Nickel	Skilling	
Florin	Pahlavi	Stuiver	
Fugio	Penny	Stumer	

Animal Crossing

In this word search, you have to find 32 words. Half of them are animals, the other half are words that can be paired with the animals to form 16 common idioms, where the animal is the second word. To help you get started, locate NIGHT and OWL.

Answer is on page 135.

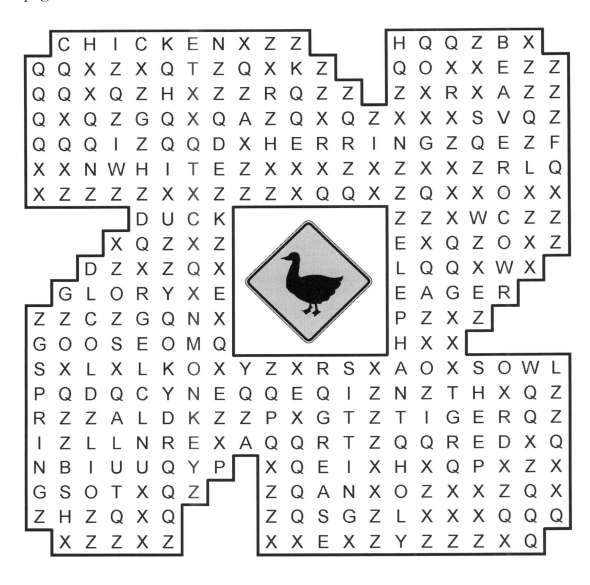

NIGHT OWL _____ _____ _____

_____ _____ _____ _____

_____ _____ _____ _____

_____ _____ _____ _____

Sudoku

Sudoku is a logic puzzle, not a math puzzle. The goal is to complete the grid in such a way that each row, column and 3x3 box contains each digit from 1 to 9.

As you go about solving each grid, make sure you never put a digit in the same row, column or box that already has that digit.

The first 12 puzzles are easy. The next 12 are a bit more difficult. The final 12 are a lot more difficult.

Whole books, websites and lives have been devoted to the subject of solving a Sudoku. If you get frustrated, you could check out these resources:

• https://www.sudokuwiki.org/Strategy_Families

• https://bestofsudoku.com/sudoku-strategy

Answers begin on page 136.

	8		2	1				7
	4					2	3	1
	2		4				5	
8	5	1			9			
9	6				5			
	3	7	1		4		9	
	7	8	9		2	5		
				7	6		8	
6		5	8			3	7	2

8		1	3	4			2	
	5		6			8		3
				9	5	1		
6				5	9			4
		3				7	5	
		5	2	3		6	8	
		9	5		8	4		6
5	7		1			2		8
3		6						

	4	8		3			9	
6	5					1		3
	3		9					
	6			5	9		2	8
		2		7		3		5
7		5			3	6	4	9
	2	3		1	5		8	
5			7		8	4	3	1
			3					

		5		4				
			5	6	2	9		
8	9	2				4		
	4		8	1	7			
	5	8				3		
2	1	6			4	8		
		7	2		6		5	
	3			8				7
5			7	3	1	6	4	8

1			5	3			7	2
	7	3	2		1	6		
								5
		1	8		7	5	6	
			1					9
		7			4	2		1
	3	6					5	4
2		4	7				1	6
9		8		6	5			

9		1	4	6				5
		8		2				
		6		3		7	8	1
	4	2			6			7
	8					4		3
				4		1	9	
	1		6		3			
	3	7			9		1	4
6	9				4	2	3	8

3		7						
8	5	2	4	1		9		
					2			8
	1		7	8				2
				2	4	6	9	
2	7			3	5	8		1
		9		7		4	2	
	2	5		4				9
				9	1		3	5

2	1				7	9		3
	3	4	9			1		
		8		1	3		6	2
		2		3			1	9
	7	9		5		6	3	
3				7	9		2	
		5			6		8	
		7		2		3	9	
	6				8		5	

	9		4			8	6	
			1	2			7	
	7			6				3
	6	1		9		3	4	
	8		2			5		
9	2					6		1
	4		6		1	7		
3	5	6		8				9
7	1	8	3					

	4	9	7	5	3	2	6	
	3	5		8	6			4
7					1			8
6		2		3	8	7	4	
	7	8		6	2	1	9	
	5			4	7	6		
						8		
							5	6
9	6					3		7

9			7		1		2	5
		2					3	
	7	5			3	6		1
					5	2		
7	5	1		2	9		4	6
	9	6		1				8
	2		3		5			
	4	3		6	8			
	6	7			1			

Sudoku #12

5		3	2					
6	9		3				2	
			9		5			
4	5	8			6	2	3	
	3					4		9
7	6						8	
	8	2	5	7	3			1
		6			1	9		
		5	6		9	8		3

	2		3	1		9	5	
		6		7		8		1
		9	6			3		7
6						5		8
	7			5			6	9
8	4							
	6	4		2	5			
5			8		6			4
2		7	1	4				

Sudoku #14

		3	1					
9					6	1	3	7
						8		2
					7			
		5		2	3			
		8				4		1
8	5			3	9		1	4
3	1	7		4		9		
				5		2	8	

7					5		3	
2	4	6		1			8	
		9				4		6
3			1	5			7	
4	8		2	7		6		
		1		4			2	3
1	6	7	5	9				
8				3	1			2
								7

5					9		2	6
		8	1					7
	7	3	8	6	2			
		6	5					2
4	3			9		5	6	8
			7		6		1	
						9		1
				8	7	2	5	
		9				6		

3	4			8				
7	6				1			9
2		5						1
				9				2
6		2				5	9	
		4			5	3		
1		7		4	2			8
					9	7		
8			1	7			6	4

Sudoku #18

					1		7	
1			8			9	4	
		6	4					2
5	9		7	1				
6	1				3	7	9	
		8	9		6			5
		5			4	3		
4	6	7	3		2	5		
	8			7		4		

8		5	9	6		4	1	
	3				7			
			5	8			9	7
			8	2			3	
	5		7	3				4
3		2			5	6		
2	8			1				5
		7	3			2	6	
	1			7				

Sudoku #20

6	5	3				1	7	
					6	5	9	
4	1		5	3				
	8	6		9	5		4	7
1	9					8	2	
			6	8		9		
			8		4			
			3				5	
7		4		5	9	6	8	

					6			2
3		6	1					
1						5	7	
5	6	1	7					8
9			8			3	4	
		8		5				7
8			6	4	5	7		
	7		2			9	5	3
		5						

Sudoku #22

3				2				
	4	5	3		9			2
	6		5	7		9		
	8					1		
4		6	9	3	2		7	
	7	9	1	6		4		
	3		6					1
				9	4			6
6			2			7		

							2	
			5	8	6		4	9
4	5		2	9		1		
	7					9		1
6	2		4	1			3	
			3				7	
8			9	5				
			6	4	1	7		8
		1				4	9	

Sudoku #24

	5	9			1			
			2	9				
		4		5		9	8	
	3		4		2	1	5	
				8				2
			1					6
	2	5			6	4		
7	4		3		5	6	9	
1	6	3		4				8

Sudoku #25

			6			1		8
4					5			
7	8			1			4	
	7	1				9		
			3					
		5		4				7
						5	2	1
2	9					6		

Sudoku #26

							1	
		7	4					
9	5	2		7	8	6		
3	6					9		
			8					
	4			3				7
		4					5	
1			6		2		3	8

	1		7	4				
								7
9				8		3	5	
1	9			6			7	8
	7							
8		5					2	
	2			7				
	4		5					6
						1	4	

Sudoku #28

	6				5		9	
	8		4	1				
								5
3			6			2	4	
5				9				
	4		7					6
						8		
8						9	2	
	5	1		7				

		9			7		1	5
4			3			8		
3				9	1			2
							6	
	5			6		9		
		4			5			
			7	3				
	2		8					
	3						7	8

Sudoku #30

	2	5					3	
	9	3	8			5	1	
								6
7						1		8
	4			3			7	
							6	
	8		6	1				
			4			3	5	2
		7	3					

7				2			5	
1	6				9			7
		8						2
	9		3			8		
				6				1
			5	1				6
			7	8		1		
				3				
8		6						9

Sudoku #32

				3		5		
					5	4	7	1
	1	6		7				
2	5				6			
			4					3
9				8				
		8	7			6		9
	2	7		4			8	

	9				8			
		2					1	5
6	3							2
9			2	4				
				7	6	2		
						7	4	
	6			8				
	7		9		4			
4		8				1		6

Sudoku #34

			4	1		5		
					8			
9	5			2				
7	6					8		5
			2		3	4		7
		3		5				6
8		7		9				
							6	
	2	1				7		

	8	7					1	
6			3		2			4
			5		8			
7				9			2	
						4		
	9				4			
					5	9		3
	3		4					2
9		5		6				

Sudoku #36

4					9			
6	7			5	3			
2					1	5		9
	8		2	1			4	
		1	3					
								6
			6					
		3		7		9	2	
		2				7		1

Answers

State School
1. Arizona (1987 movie)
2. Montana (Television series)
3. Washington (get it?)
4. Maine
5. Colorado
6. Kentucky, Massachusetts, Pennsylvania, Virginia
7. Mi**chi**gan, Mississip**pi**, New Me**xi**co, **Rho**de Island

Things That Have _____
Things that have wings:
Jumbo jet, Nighthawk, Blue jay, Fruit bat, Ladybug,
Spruce Goose, White House (West Wing), Horsefly,
Yellow bird

Skeleton Crew
Aerosmith, *Lord of the Thighs*
Beatles, *I Want to Hold your Hand*
Funkadelic, *(Not Just) Knee Deep*
John Denver, *Sunshine On My Shoulders*
Kenny Loggins, *Footloose*
Shakira, *Hips Don't Lie*
ZZ Top, *Legs*

Ghosts in the Machines
SMARTPHONE (PHANTOM)
RANDOMIZER (DEMON)
TRINISCOPE (SPIRIT)
NICKELODEON (EIDOLON)
VIEWFINDER (FIEND)
IMMOBILIZER (ZOMBIE)
SNOWPLOUGH (GHOUL)

Rack Your Brain #1
DELO DELT DERO DOER DOLE DOLT DORE DORT
DOTE EDDO EORL LODE LORD LORE LOTE OLDE
ORLE REDD REDO RODE ROED ROLE ROTE ROTL
TELD TOED TOLD TOLE TORE TROD
DOLED DOTED DOTER DROLE ODDER OLDER
RODED ROTED TODDE TOLED TRODE
DORTED LORDED RETOLD TODDLE
TODDLER

Rack Your Brain #2
ADRY AIRY AMID AMIR ARID ARMY DAMP DARI
DIMP DIYA DRAM DRAP DRAY DRIP MAID MAIR
MARD MARY MIRY PADI PAID PAIR PARD PIMA PRAD
PRAM PRAY PRIM RAID RAMI RAMP RIAD RIMA RIMY
YARD YIRD
DAIRY DAMPY DIARY DIRAM MARDY MARID PADRI
PARDI PARDY PRIMA PRIMY RAPID YAIRD
MIDPAY MYRIAD
PYRAMID

Skip to My Lou
1. Lou Diamond Phillips (portrayed Ritchie Valens in the movie)
2. Lou Rawls (singer, composer)
3. Lou Ferrigno (Bill Bixby was Dr. Bruce Banner, Ferrigno was the Hulk)
4. Lou Costello (Bud Abbott and Lou Costello were a comedy team during the 1940s and 1950s)
5. Lou Grant (Ed Asner played the title role)

12 Signs of Opposition
ARIES & LIBRA	TAURUS & SCORPIO
GEMINI & SAGITTARIUS	CANCER & CAPRICORN
LEO & AQUARIUS	VIRGO & PISCES

That's the Pits!
STOMACH, BARBECUE, ARM, APRICOTS, MOSH,
OLIVES, CHERRIES, PEACH, PLUM, NECTARINES

Supreme Kart
Moose tat=Tomatoes; Ripped lace=Apple cider;
Boar's feet=Roast beef; Matte toner=Rotten meat;
Old army bed=Moldy bread; Tube wetters=Sweet butter;
Bent-up oars=Bean sprout; Tattered bowl=Bottled water;
Cob bar trays=Baby carrots; Idle silk mop=Spoiled milk;
Rusted mangers=Mustard greens;
Glassed drains=Salad dressing; Fur bride suit=Bruised fruit;
Scab thickeners=Chicken breasts;
Eel-faced turtle=Red leaf lettuce;
Ersatz pullet ends=Unsalted pretzels;
Huge armpit baster=Hamburger patties;
Porous teeth rakes=Porterhouse steak

Wild Weekend at Westville U.
Warblers = Brawlers; echoing mom = homecoming;
charming = marching; race from pen = performance;
the genie = eighteen; gurney sots = youngsters;
minor panda = prima donna; here declare = cheerleader;
peon rams = open arms; bum elf = fumble;
backed the kill = kicked the ball; racquet bark = quarterback

Indicatory
Level 1
BEGIN (2) Being, Binge; BELOW (2) Bowel, Elbow
FILOS (1) Foils; GHOST (2) Gosht, Goths
GIMPY (1) Pigmy; GORSY (1) Gyros; HORST (1) Short

Level 2
ADEPT (3) Apted, Pated, Taped; AGIST (2) Gaits, Staig
BEINS (2) Benis, Bines; CHIMO (2) Mochi, Ohmic
CHIRT (2) Crith, Richt; FINOS (2) Foins, Infos
GLOPS (2) Golps, Splog; KNOPS (2) Knosp, Ponks
MOPSY (2) Myops, Yomps

Level 3
ABORT (2) Boart, Tabor; ADIOS (2) Aidos, Dosai
AHINT (2) Haint, Hiant; AMORT (1) Morat
CHIKS (1) Hicks; CHIVY (1) Vichy; DEFIS (1) Fides
FLORS (1) Rolfs

Level 4
CEILS (3) Ciels, Clies, Slice
DELOS (5) Doles, Lodes, Losed, Solde, Soled
DEMOS (3) Domes, Modes, Mosed
LOPS (4) Lopes, Olpes, Poles, Slope
FIRST (3) Frist, Frits, Rifts

Level 5
ABERS (6) Bares, Baser, Bears, Braes, Saber, Sabre
ACERS (8) Acres, Cares, Carse, Escar, Races, Scare, Scrae, Serac
DEILS (9) Delis, Diels, Eilds, Idles, Isled, Sidle, Sield, Siled, Slide
DEIST (6) Diets, Dites, Edits, Sited, Stied, Tides

Bonus
Each word is also an alphagram, meaning that its letters are in alphabetical order. That's why they come before their related anagrams in a dictionary. By the way, *indicatory* is an anagram of *dictionary*.

Answers

Ungodly Hour
(Undo Roughly) Shiva: Hindu god of destruction
(Nod, Holy Guru) The Temporal Lord: In Sikhism, Guru is the source of all knowledge which is almighty
(Go Dun Hourly) Plutus: Greek god of wealth
(Oh run, old guy!) Hermes: Greek god: "messenger of the gods"
(Do Hurl Young) Ganga: Hindu goddess who drowned 7 of her 8 children in the Ganges River
(Loud Horn Guy) Gabriel: Archangel who blows horn on Judgement Day
(You Hung, Lord!) Odin: Norse god who hanged himself on the cosmological tree, Yggdrasil
(Hold Your Gun) Athena: Greek goddess of military strategy
(Oh Unruly Dog) Anubis: Egyptian god, usually depicted in human form, with a canine head.
(Unholy Gourd) Leza: Bantu deity, gave three gourds to a hummingbird to give to humans; the third contained sickness, death and dangerous animals
(Round Ugly Ho) Venus: Roman goddess of prostitutes

Jimmy vs. Peter
JIMMY BARTHOLOMEW OLSEN
Arrowverse, Chloe Sullivan, Daily Planet, Lucy Lane, Marc McClure, Metropolis, Perry White

PETER BENJAMIN PARKER
Daily Bugle, Gwen Stacy, J. Jonah Jameson, Liz Allan, Marvel Cinematic Universe, Mary Jane Watson, Midtown High School, Tobey Maguire, Uncle Ben

***CKED UP
1. RACKED UP, 2. BUCKED UP, 3. PACKED UP,
4. MUCKED UP, 5. BACKED UP, 6. MOCKED UP,
7. PICKED UP, 8. HACKED UP, 9. TACKED UP,
10. JACKED UP, 11. LICKED UP, 12. LOCKED UP,
13. SUCKED UP, 14. KICKED UP

Bear Necessities
Baby Bear carried the Goldilocks doll (clue 2.)
Mama Bear can't carry the frying pan, because she wouldn't be able to carry anything else (clues 1 and 3.) So, she carried the family photo and the shotgun, Papa Bear carried the reading glasses and the fishing rod (clue 3) and Baby Bear carried the frying pan.

Auction
The baseball card cost 100, Colin spent 200 and the antique plate cost 400 (clue 2.) Adam spent 400 (clue 1) so he bought the antique plate. The action figure cost 200 (clue 4), so Colin bought it. By elimination, the silver dollar cost 300 and Debbie bought it (clue 3), and Billy bought the baseball card.

Adam spent 400 on the antique plate. Debbie spent 300 on the silver dollar. Colin spent 200 on the action figure. Billy spent 100 on the baseball card.

Extracurricular Activities
Football can't be Monday or Friday; soccer can't be Thursday or Friday; gymnastics can't be Monday or Tuesday (clue 9.) Reba, who practices Monday and Tuesday (clue 8), doesn't play football or gymnastics, she plays soccer. Reba doesn't play guitar (clue 4) or saxophone (clue 7), so her Tuesday activity is piano, and she has soccer practice on Mondays.

Vernon plays football and guitar (clue 4), leaving the final sport, gymnastics, to Claire (clue 3) and the final instrument, the saxophone, to Dustin (clue 7.)

Dustin can't practice on Tuesdays (clue 6.) He practices on Thursdays (clue 5.) Vernon can't practice guitar on Tuesdays (clue 6.) He practices guitar on Thursdays (clue 5) and football on Wednesdays (clue 2.) Claire practices on Fridays (clues 6 and 9.)

Monday	Reba	Soccer;
Tuesday	Reba	Piano;
Wednesday	Vernon	Football;
Thursday	Vernon	Guitar;
Thursday	Dustin	Saxophone;
Friday	Claire	Gymnastics

Conspira-SEA
Kraken is 1908; Black Sea is 1971; Sargasso Sea is neither 1908 nor 1966; Hydra is not 1966 or 1971 (clue 2.)

Ross Sea is 2004; Red Sea is not 1957; neither Scylla nor Charybdis are 1957 or 2004 (clue 5.)

Hydra is 1895 (clue 1.)

Oman Sea is 1895 and Sargasso Sea is 1933 (clue 9.)

Charybdis can only be 1908 or 1946 (clue 7) but Kraken is 1908 (clue 2), so Charybdis is 1946, East China Sea is 1957 and Plesiosaur is 1933.

Adriatic Sea, Leviathan and Cieren Croin are not 1966 (clue 10.)

Adriatic Sea after Leviathan, which is after 1946 (clue 4), so Adriatic is 1972 and Leviathan is 1957 or 1971.

Yellow Sea can only be 1908 (clue 3.)

Tyrrhenian Sea and Basking Shark are not 1966 (clue 6), so Tyrrhenian Sea is 1946 and Red Sea is 1966.

Because Red Sea is 1966, clues 2 and 5 describe all nine documents. Therefore, Scylla can't be 1966 or 1971. It must be 1972.

Makara is 1966.

Basking Shark is before 1966 (clue 8), so it is 1957.

By elimination, Cirein Croin is 2004, leaving Leviathan as 1971.

1895	Oman Sea Monster	Hydra
1908	Yellow Sea Sailor's Log	Kraken
1933	Sargasso Sea Diary	Plesiosaur
1946	Tyrrhenian Sea Terror	Charybdis
1957	East China Sea Dossier	Basking Shark
1966	Red Sea Report	Makara
1971	Black Sea Report	Leviathan
1972	Adriatic Sea File	Scylla
2004	Ross Sea Papers	Cirein Croin

Answers

Easy as Pie

Instruments of Torture
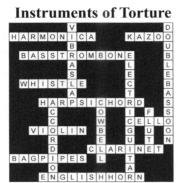

Alarming Final*

*Alarming Final = Anagram Fill in

Hammerin' Hank

Bob's Your Uncle

On the Cutting Edge

Swift Response

Steampunk Contraption
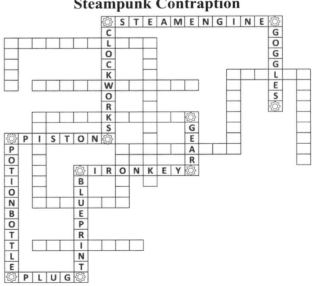

Famous Pigs

Fruit Fill
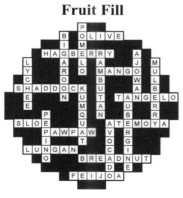

Answers

Time is Money, But Money Saves Time

Scenario F is the correct answer. The key to accepting Rumpelstiltskin's deal is that Cinderella works on her gown while traveling to and from the forest! She'll have more than enough time to finish the gown when she returns.

Scenarios A, C and E fail because Cinderella simply can't afford to hire the Bibbidi-Bobbidi-Boo Livery Company.

Scenarios B and D fail because Cinderella ends up with two pairs of shoes.

Scenario G fails because it exceeds her budget. The material from Red cost 30 silver coins. Jack spends four days on the mushroom quest (including travel), which costs 80 silver coins, leaving Cinderella 10 silver coins short.

National Security Amnesia

#1: PUF**FB**IRD	#2: TWI**CE**	#3: RA**DIA**TE
#4: **DOJ**O	#5: OR**DEAL**	#6: P**LAT**FORM
#7: FL**OTS**AM	#8: IN**SANE**	#9: MAGI**CIA**N

It's a Numbers Game

Read aloud:
HYPER 10 SION (hypertension), CA 9 (canine),
FR 8 ER (freighter), 7 TIES (seventies),CLASS 6 (classics),
5 R (fiver), EN 4 CE (enforce), 3 FOLD (threefold),
2 THY (toothy), UN 1 TED (unwanted)

Homework Helpers

The first clue is a red herring. The two students who received an F and the student who received a C were the three that got caught. Angela received a D (clue 4), so she is the one who got away with cheating.

Match Wits

1. Hardheaded	9. Seersucker
2. Pickpocket	10. Rearranger
3. Forefinger	11. Barebacked
4. Landlocked	12. Lackluster
5. Stepsister	13. Sideswipes
6. Bookbinder	14. Baseballer
7. Temptingly	15. Slipstream
8. Woodworker	16. Songstress

Oh, My Nose!

1. From top left to bottom right: Marcia, Carol, Greg, Jan, Alice, Peter, Cindy, Mike and Bobby
2. Architect
3. Sam Franklin (he owned a butcher shop)
4. Grand Canyon
5. Benedict Arnold (if you guessed George Washington, that is who Peter wanted to play)
6. George Glass
7. Pork chops and applesauce
8. 4222 Clinton way (William Clinton became the 42nd president of the United States.)
9. Peter was fired from his first job as a bicycle mechanic. Later, Marcia fired him from his job at the ice cream shop.
10. Carol Ann Tyler Martin Brady; (Mike Paul Brady)
11. Peter / Arthur Owens (*Two Petes in a Pod*);
   Alice / Emma (*Sergeant Emma*);
   Carol / Grandma Connie Hutchins and
   Mike / Grandpa Hank Brady (*You're Never Too Old*)

Bonus: Sherwood Schwartz created both shows. Jim Backus appeared on both shows. He was Thurston Howell III on Gilligan's Island. On The Brady Bunch, he appeared in the first two episodes of Season 3 as Zachariah T. Brown and in Season 5, Episode 21 as Henry Matthews (Mike's second boss.)

Cryptograms

1. "My mother's love has always been a sustaining force for our family, and one of my greatest joys is seeing her integrity, her compassion, her intelligence reflected in my daughters."
- Michelle Obama

2. "A wise man can learn more from a foolish question than a fool can learn from a wise answer."
- Bruce Lee

3. "I used to do the beat box. A friend of mine, he was the rapper and after, we'd be doing a block party or something or a house party, and he's gettin' all the attention and I'd end up with a handful of spit, you know, from doing the beats."
- DMX

4. "It was amazing that a play that seems dated in this world... A man whose best friend is a six-foot white rabbit... But it caught on, especially with young people - they surprised me most of all."
- James Stewart

5. "We do not remember days, we remember moments."
- Cesare Pavese

6. "After 'The Matrix,' I cannot wear sunglasses. As soon as I put them on, people recognize me."
- Carrie-Anne Moss

7. "We can easily forgive a child who is afraid of the dark; the real tragedy of life is when men are afraid of the light."
- Plato

8. "There's, like, a dark needle or a nail that lives at the back of all of our heads, and that's your fear."
- Sandra Oh

9. "History, despite its wrenching pain, cannot be unlived, but if faced with courage, need not be lived again."
- Maya Angelou

10. "When you love someone, the best thing you can offer is your presence. How can you love if you are not there?"
- Thich Nhat Hanh

11. "Keep your face always toward the sunshine - and shadows will fall behind you."
- Walt Whitman

12. My horse is a cereal killer. He goes through three pounds of oats every day.

Answers

Cryptograms (continued)

13. I grew up in the forests of Northern California. Most of my friends are also trees, so you might say I am poplar.

14. The astronauts on the International Space Station prefer to sip cosmos and eat Milky Way candy bars.

15. "You want the moon? Just say the word and I'll throw a lasso around it and pull it down."
-George Bailey in It's a Wonderful Life

16. Football would be easy to understand if the rules didn't change all the time.

17. A gherkin walks up to a beet and says, "Lettuce make music." So they turned into a piccolo and a drum.

18. "Swearing was invented as a compromise between running away and fighting."
– Finley Peter Dunne

19. A priest, a rabbi and a minister walk into a bar. The bartender looks at them and says, "What is this – a joke?"

20. A man walked into a bar with his alligator and asked the bartender, "Do you serve lawyers here?"
"Sure do," replied the bartender. "Good," said the man. "Give me a beer, and I'll have a lawyer for my gator."

21. "The hard part about being a bartender is figuring out who is drunk and who is just stupid."
– Richard Braunstein

22. "The trouble with having an open mind, of course, is that people will insist on coming along and trying to put things in it."
- Terry Pratchett

23. "To the mind that is still, the whole universe surrenders."
- Lao Tzu

24. A manual helped me restore my vintage car. I misread the lookup table and switched the fan belt with the seat belt!

25. "There are people who go in a direction that you'd have thought their name would, sort of, turn them right against."
— John Hoyland, journalist

26. Oliver North and Kanye West are the most reliable people to ask for directions.

27. "I learned long ago, never to wrestle with a pig. You get dirty, and besides, the pig likes it."
- George Bernard Shaw

28. "Big doesn't necessarily mean better. Sunflowers aren't better than violets."
- Edna Ferber

29. "To learn to read is to light a fire; every syllable that is spelled out is a spark."
- Victor Hugo

30. "When you are not practicing, someone else is getting better."
- Allen Iverson

31. "You better cut the pizza in four pieces because I'm not hungry enough to eat six."
- Yogi Berra

32. Tom Swifties are awful puns. See how many you can guess. If you get stuck, another puzzle in this book has all of the words.
"Cupid shot me," Tom said _____.
"I joined the navy," Tom said _____.
"I only season my pot roast with sage and rosemary," Tom said _____.
"Sue me," Tom said _____.
(FYI: This is not the hidden puzzle!)

33. "Don't talk unless you can improve the silence."
- Jorge Luis Borges

34. Crimson
   Pink
   Carmine
   Rosewood
   Cordovan
   Garnet
   Vermilion
   Salmon
   Cinnabar
   Scarlet
   Tomato

35. Mobile
   Princess
   Cordless
   Videophone
   Flip phone
   Trimline
   Rotary Phone
   Satellite phone
   Smartphone
   iPhone

36. Sandals
   Clogs
   Espadrilles
   Jellies
   Moccasins
   Loafers
   Sneakers
   Pumps
   Stilettos

37. Saint Bernard
   Basset Hound
   Dachshund
   Bull Terrier
   Pekingese
   Irish Setter
   Whippet
   Golden Retriever
   Samoyed
   Dalmatian
   Afghan Hound
   German Shepherd
   Pug
   Leonberger

Answers

Marching Orders

Row 1: Letters increment by one and rotate clockwise by one

Row 2: Letters and numbers increment by one; Letters rotate counter-clockwise by one; numbers rotate clockwise by one

Row 3: Letters increment by one; clockwise rotation increments by one (0, 1, 2, 3, 4, 5)

Row 4: +1, +2, +1, +4, +1, +8, +1, +16 = 34

Row 5: (B) Circles in group alternate between black and white; triangle alternates between black and white

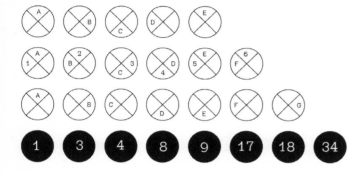

Shrinkage

AVERAGE, BANDAGE, BONDAGE, HOSTAGE, MASSAGE, MESSAGE, MILLAGE, OVERAGE, PASSAGE, PEERAGE, PEONAGE, PILLAGE, PLUMAGE, POSTAGE, PRESAGE, RESTAGE, SEEPAGE, VANTAGE, VILLAGE, VOLTAGE

Bonus words:
BASTION, MERSION, MILLION, PASSION, PEREION, PILLION, TERSION, TOMPION, VERSION, AVERSION, PAVILION, PRESSION, IMPRESSION

Out of Order

HEAT, WATER, SMOKING, ELECTRICITY, REFRIGERATOR
WHACKS CEILING

Chuck Wagon

STEW, FISH, BEANS, BURGERS, HOTDOGS, BAKED POTATO
WITHERSPOON

Arboretum

TEAK, BIRCH, DOGWOOD, SYCAMORE
DISEMBARK

Rich Man, Poor Man

1. TINKER: bricoleur, handyman, factotum
2. TAILOR: couturier, modiste, sartor
3. SOLDIER: condottiere, dogface, doughboy
4. SAILOR: jacktar, leatherneck, shellback
5. RICH MAN: affluent, millionaire, prosperous
6. POOR MAN: bankrupt, destitute, penurious
7. BEGGARMAN: guttersnipe, palliard*, spanger
8. THIEF: bandit, cutpurse, purloiner
* *This obsolete word is not to be confused with **paillard**.*

Alphabet Soup

ABCDEF = 8 letters: BOLDFACE, FEEDBACK
GHIJKL = 9 letters: JACKLIGHT
MNOP = 6 letters: EPONYM, IMPONE, MOPANE (*small South African tree; also* MOPANI), MOPING, NYMPHO, PHENOM, POMPON, POTMAN, POTMEN, TAMPON, TOMPON (*same as tampon*), TOPMAN, TOPMEN
QRS = 5 letters: QURSH (*monetary unit of Saudi Arabia*)
TUVW = 10 letters: LIVERWURST
XYZ = 7 letters: ZOOTAXY (*systematic zoology*)

Poetic PUN-ishment

1. Happy Birthday: BENIGN
2. Stars In Your Eyes?: ORBITAL INSERTION
3. Chasing Puck: SPITTLE of the RINKS
4. Risqué Business: BOARD STIFF
5. Secretary Estate: CONDO LEASE ARISE*
6. Soft Shoulder: TURNED to a PILLOW ASSAULT

The remaining words, listed alphabetically:

A BLATANTLY CRUDE DITTY EXACTLY FIVE LINES MAKE ONE STANZA THAT'S WITTY.
(A Limerick)
* Condoleezza Rice served as the 66th United States secretary of state from 2005 to 2009.

Rock, Paper, Scissors, BOOM! #1

Rock, Paper, Scissors, BOOM! #2

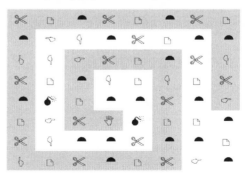

Answers

Elements of Style

B O O Ts; B U Sb Y; Br I Tc He S; Br Og U Es; C Ra V At; Co At; F O N Ta Ge; Ho O P S K Ir Ts; K Ni C K Er B O C K Er S (K Ni C K Er S); La Ce Pa N Ti Es; Mo C Ca Si N S; O V Er Co At; P I Na F O Re; Pa N Ts; Pa N Ts U I Ts; Po N C Ho; Po U La In Es; Ra In Co At; Ra In S U I Ts; S As H; S H Ir Ts; S Ho Es; S K Ir Ts; S U B F U S C S (S U B F U S K S)*; S U I Ts; Sc Ar V Es; Sm O C K; Ti Es; U Nd I Es

* Academic dress of the University of Oxford

Pyramid Scheme

Did you suspect the food pyramid?

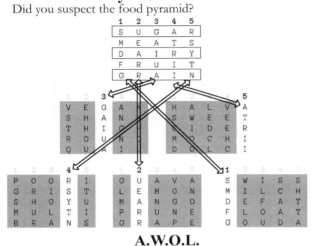

A.W.O.L.

D: ABODE, CODE, DAUNT, DIVA, LADING, GRADES
E: BELLY, GERM, CHECK, HOMELY, MELD, WELT
S: BASING, DAISY, INSET, SAVAGE, PASTED, WHOSE
E: GUNMEN, HECK, MELLOW, PERSON, FLUENT, DREW
R: DRAM, SCORE, COVER, DOZER, RUTS, PARTIES
T: WHITE, BUST, HUTCH, MEAT, SPITE, CRATE
E: MESSY, OUTLET, OYSTER, PEBBLY, CLOTHE, TENTH
R: DEVOUR, CLEAR, ROOK, ERASE, HARES, MARCH

This is tricky, because quite a few suitable replacements can complete the list of words. But only one combination reveals the related word, DESERTER.

(If you chose VERANTER, Google says that is Dutch for *change*. Perhaps a hint to try again? LOL)

Punagrams

1. BE ABOVE DAWN = BOB AND WEAVE
2. KNOBBIEST BONDAGE = BOSTON BAKED BEING
3. ONE LOADED KEY = YANKEE DOODLE
4. HUNGRY? ADD GOO = GROUNDHOG DAY
5. UM, OBLATION = OUT ON A LIMB
6. FLEE IF POI = LIFE OF PIE

League of Bad Bowlers

Frame 1
Strike: **DOWNFALLEN**
Spares: Allow (Fend); Dowel (Flan); Dwell (Anon); Eland (Flow, Fowl, Wolf); Endow (Fall, Flan); Felon (Dawn, Land, Lawn, Wand); Flown (Dale, Deal, Dean, Elan, Lade, Land, Lane, Lead, Lean, Lend); Laden (Flow, Fowl, Wolf); Llano (Fend, Wend); Lowed (Flan); Nodal (Flew); Olden (Fawn, Flan, Flaw, Lawn); Owned (Fall, Flan)

Frame 2
Strike: **STRIKELESS**
Spares: Ester (Ilks, Kiss, Silk, Skis); Isles (Erst, Rest, Trek); Keels (Sirs, Sits, Stir); Kilts (Seer, Sees, Sere); Kites (Less); Leeks (Sirs, Sits, Stir); Leers (Kiss, Kits, Sits, Skis, Skit); Liker (Sets); Likes (Erst, Rest, Sets); Lists (Ekes, Reek, Seek, Seer, Sere); Reeks (List, Silt, Sits, Slit); Reels (Kiss, Kits, Sits, Skis, Skit); Reset (Ilks, Kiss, Silk, Skis); Rests (Elks, Ilks, Isle, Leis, Lies, Like, Silk); Riles (Sets); Rises (Elks, Lest, Lets); Risks (Eels, Else, Lees, Lest, Lets, Tees); Rites (Elks, Less); Seeks (List, Silt, Slit, Stir); Seers (Ilks, Kilt, Kits, List, Silk, Silt, Skit, Slit); Silks (Erst, Rest, Seer, Sere, Tees, Tree); Silts (Ekes, Reek, Seek, Seer, Sere); Sires (Elks, Lest, Lets); Sises (Trek); Sites (Elks); Skeet (Sirs); Skier (Less, Lest, Lets); Skies (Erst, Lest, Lets, Rest); Skirt (Eels, Else, Lees, Less, Sees); Skits (Eels, Else, Leer, Lees, Reel, Seer, Sere); Sleek (Sirs, Sits, Stir); Sleet (Irks, Kiss, Risk, Sirs, Skis); Slier (Sets); Slits (Ekes, Reek, Seek, Seer, Sere); Steel (Irks, Kiss, Risk, Sirs, Skis); Steer (Ilks, Kiss, Silk, Skis); Sties (Elks); Stirs (Eels, Ekes, Elks, Else, Keel, Leek, Lees, Seek); Terse (Ilks, Kiss, Silk, Skis); Tiers (Elks, Less); Tikes (Less); Tires (Elks, Less); Trees (Ilks, Kiss, Silk, Skis); Treks (Isle, Leis, Less, Lies); Tress (Elks, Ilks, Isle, Leis, Lies, Like, Silk); Tries (Elks, Less); Trike (Less)

Frame 3
Strike: **FINGERBOWL**
Spares: Begin (Flow, Fowl, Wolf); Being (Flow, Fowl, Wolf); Below (Frig, Grin, Ring); Bilge (Worn); Binge (Flow, Fowl, Wolf); Bingo (Flew); Blown (Fire, Frig, Rife); Bowel (Frig, Grin, Ring); Bower (Ling); Brief (Glow, Gown, Long); Brine (Flog, Flow, Fowl, Glow, Golf, Wolf); Bring (Flew, Floe, Flow, Fowl, Wolf); Brown (File, Lief, Life); Elbow (Frig, Grin, Ring); Elfin (Brow, Grow); Feign (Blow, Bowl, Brow); Felon (Brig); Fiber (Glow, Gown, Long); Fibre (Glow, Gown, Long); Filer (Bong, Gown); Finer (Blog, Blow, Bowl, Glob, Glow); Flier (Bong, Gown); Fling (Bore, Brew, Brow, Robe, Wore); Flown (Berg, Bier, Brie, Brig, Gibe); Frown (Bile, Gibe, Glib); Grief (Blow, Bowl); Groin (Blew, Flew); Growl (Fine); Grown (Bile, File, Lief, Life); Infer (Blog, Blow, Bowl, Glob, Glow); Lifer (Bong, Gown); Lingo (Brew); Noble (Frig); Owner (Glib); Reign (Blow, Bowl, Flow, Fowl, Wolf); Rifle (Bong, Gown); Robin (Flew); Wring (Bole, Floe, Lobe); Wrong (Bile, File, Lief, Life)

I.O.U.
Bilko, Bok choy, Broccoli, Broccolini, Choy sum, Rubicon

Conga Words
1. TUNA, 2. NASAL, 3. SALAD, 4. LADDER, 5. DERBY, 6. BYTE, 7. TEPID, 8. DWELL, 9. ELLIPSE, 10. PSEUDONYM, 11. NYMPH, 12. PHONETIC, 13. TICKLE, 14. KLEPTOMANIA, 15. IAMBIC, 16. BICENTENNIAL, 17. ALABASTER, 18. ASTEROID, 19. IDEA, 20. EASEL

Navy Beans
You can sink the fleet with these beans: BLACK, EDAMAME, FAVA, GARBANZO, GREEN, KIDNEY and PINTO

Answers

Engine Engine #9
The following trains are not involved in collisions, because they have the track to themselves: EJ1, EJ2, EJ4, CC1, CC2 and CC5. EJ3 and CC3 both leave their respective stations at the same time and will collide somewhere along the track. The same is true of EJ5 and CC4, as well as EJ6 and CC6.

From the picture, we can see that the collision occurs somewhere between the 30-mile and 40-mile markers. Since EJ3 travels 60 miles per hour, it will be well past the 40-mile marker before it collides with CC3. If you're mathematically inclined, you can probably work out that the two trains collide at 10:48 AM, at the 48-mile marker.

Using the same logic, CC6, traveling at 80 miles per hour, makes it to the 31-mile marker before colliding with EJ6 at 5:37 PM.

That means that the correct answer is CC4 and EJ5. If you worked it out, you would see that they collide at 1:56 PM, just past the 37-mile mark.

Pepper Pop Quiz
1. A song from the Beatle's 1967 album *Sgt. Pepper's Lonely Hearts Club Band*
2. Pepperoni
3. Bass player for the rock band Red Hot Chili Peppers
4. Peanuts' character Peppermint Patty
5. Played Sgt. Pepper Anderson on the 1970's television show, *Police Woman*
6. Peter Piper picked a peck of pickled peppers, etc.
7. Julius Peppers (kudos, if you guessed Thomas "Pepper" Johnson, although he was a defensive linebacker)
8. Pepper Potts, a character in Marvel Comics' Iron Man
9. One of the hottest chili peppers, it is a hybrid of the Ghost pepper and the habanero chili pepper
10. The pharmacist who formulated Dr Pepper

Window Shopping
Bichon Frise is a breed of dog. Corbel is a projection jutting out from a wall to support a structure above it. Dingus is a doodad, thingamijig etc. Portico is a colonnaded porch.

What Entitles These People?
The ranks are all King and the serial numbers are the regnal numbers (I-IX):

1. Francis I King of France 1515-1547
2. Robert II, King of Scots 1371-1390
3. Richard III, King of England 1483-1485
4. William IV, King of England and Ireland 1830-1837
5. James V, King of Scotland, 1512-1542
6. Charles VI, King of France, 1380-1422
7. Edward VII, King of England and Ireland 1901-1910
8. Henry VIII King of England 1509-1547
9. Louis IX King of France 1226 to 1270

If you're wondering about the hint, it refers to puzzle titles where nicknames represent the kings' names:
To be *Frank*; *Bob*'s Your Uncle; *Rich* Man Poor Man; Dollar *Bill* Y'all; *Jimmy* vs. Peter; *Chuck* Wagon; Driver's *Ed*; Hammerin' *Hank*; Skip to My *Lou*

The puzzle title was a further clue: Entitles = "*In Titles*"

What the Hex? #1
WHISTLE FOG RUN: Numerals from zero to twelve
Correct order is R N O H U F S E G I T L W

What the Hex? #2
COMB WITH KEY: Couplet from Macbeth, "*By the pricking of my thumbs, something wicked this way comes.*"
Correct order: BEIOYMTKHWC

What the Hex? #3
KELP: "*Loose lips sink ships*" (World War II propaganda poster)
Correct order: ELKP

Eight Is Not Enough
Impatiens, Impatient, Umpteenth

3 x 5 = 15
True Colors
Sepia Trout Prism = Superpatriotism
Healthy Choices?
Senna Diets Sprat = Antidepressants
Foul Play
Stomp Ruins Ankle = Unsportsmanlike
Gossip
Tabus Taint Nudes = Unsubstantiated

Dollar Bill Y'all
Neither Morocco nor Thailand match franc or kwanza (clue 1), so Angola matches kwanza (clue 6.)

Cameroon matches franc (clues 1 and 3)

Only one match has same initials (clue 4). Since Morocco can only match baht or dirham (clue 6) and Ecuador can only match manat or sucre (clue 5), Equatorial Guinea must match ekwele.

Thailand matches baht (clue 2), Turkmenistan matches manat and Ecuador matches sucre (clue 5) and Morocco matches dirham (clue 6.)

By elimination, Netherlands matches gulden.

The *final* letter of the currency is the same as the *initial* letter of the country.

Decisions, Decisions
First trip: withdraw 3 P's, 4 E's, 2 R's and 1 T to spell **PEPPERTREE**

Second trip: depending on how you withdrew ALMS, your pair of five-letter words might be one of the following:

Amass, Lamas	Amass, Slams	Lamas, Mamas
Lamas, Salsa	Llama, Lamas	Llama, Malls
Llama, Mamas	Llama, Small	Malls, Mamma
Mamas, Salsa	Mamma, Salsa	Mamma, Slams
Mamma, Small	Salsa, Llama	Salsa, Slams

To Be Frank
1. Able to = CAN
2. Awake = UP
3. Carried out = DID
4. Correct = RIGHT
5. Embark = BOARD
6. Higher Up = ABOVE
7. Into view = FORTH
8. Not crooked = STRAIGHT
9. Not present = OUT
10. Obverse = FRONT
11. Presumptuous = FORWARD
12. Voiced = SPOKEN

ABOVE + BOARD
CAN + DID
FORTH + RIGHT
OUT + SPOKEN
STRAIGHT + FORWARD
UP + FRONT

Answers

I'm Steamed Up

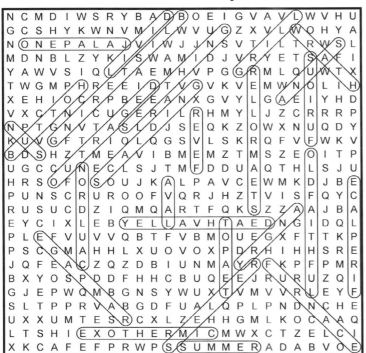

Driver's Ed

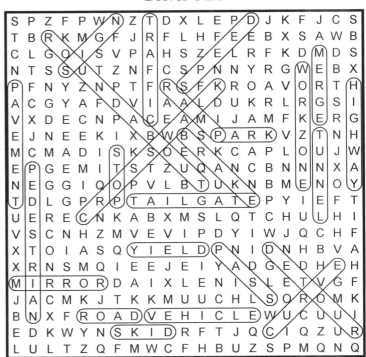

Double Trouble

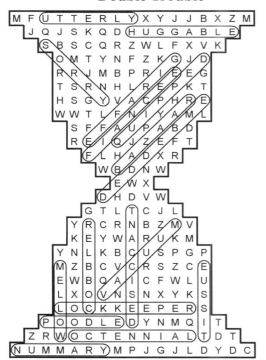

That's So Meta

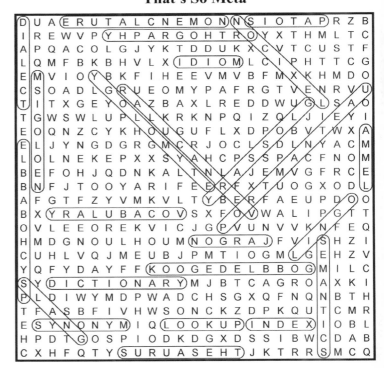

Answers

Coin Collection

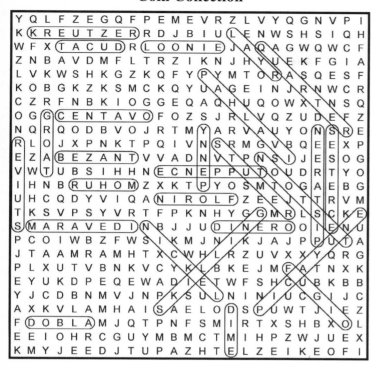

Animal Crossing

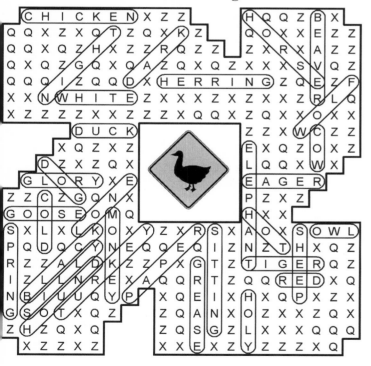

BLACK SHEEP
COLD TURKEY
DARK HORSE
EAGER BEAVER
GLORY HOUND
GREASE MONKEY
HOLY COW
HOT DOG
LONE WOLF
NIGHT OWL
PAPER TIGER
RED HERRING
SILLY GOOSE
SITTING DUCK
SPRING CHICKEN
WHITE ELEPHANT

Sudoku #1

5	8	6	2	1	3	9	4	7
7	4	9	6	5	8	2	3	1
1	2	3	4	9	7	6	5	8
8	5	1	3	2	9	7	6	4
9	6	4	7	8	5	1	2	3
2	3	7	1	6	4	8	9	5
4	7	8	9	3	2	5	1	6
3	1	2	5	7	6	4	8	9
6	9	5	8	4	1	3	7	2

Sudoku #2

8	6	1	3	4	7	9	2	5
9	5	7	6	1	2	8	4	3
4	3	2	8	9	5	1	6	7
6	2	8	7	5	9	3	1	4
1	9	3	4	8	6	7	5	2
7	4	5	2	3	1	6	8	9
2	1	9	5	7	8	4	3	6
5	7	4	1	6	3	2	9	8
3	8	6	9	2	4	5	7	1

Sudoku #3

1	4	8	5	3	7	2	9	6
6	5	9	8	4	2	1	7	3
2	3	7	9	6	1	8	5	4
3	6	4	1	5	9	7	2	8
9	8	2	4	7	6	3	1	5
7	1	5	2	8	3	6	4	9
4	2	3	6	1	5	9	8	7
5	9	6	7	2	8	4	3	1
8	7	1	3	9	4	5	6	2

Sudoku #4

1	6	5	9	4	8	7	3	2
3	7	4	5	6	2	9	8	1
8	9	2	1	7	3	4	6	5
9	4	3	8	1	7	5	2	6
7	5	8	6	2	9	3	1	4
2	1	6	3	5	4	8	7	9
4	8	7	2	9	6	1	5	3
6	3	1	4	8	5	2	9	7
5	2	9	7	3	1	6	4	8

Sudoku #5

1	6	9	5	3	8	4	7	2
5	7	3	2	4	1	6	9	8
8	4	2	6	7	9	1	3	5
4	2	1	8	9	7	5	6	3
3	8	5	1	2	6	7	4	9
6	9	7	3	5	4	2	8	1
7	3	6	9	1	2	8	5	4
2	5	4	7	8	3	9	1	6
9	1	8	4	6	5	3	2	7

Sudoku #6

9	7	1	4	6	8	3	2	5
3	5	8	7	2	1	9	4	6
4	2	6	9	3	5	7	8	1
1	4	2	3	9	6	8	5	7
7	8	9	5	1	2	4	6	3
5	6	3	8	4	7	1	9	2
2	1	4	6	8	3	5	7	9
8	3	7	2	5	9	6	1	4
6	9	5	1	7	4	2	3	8

Sudoku #7

3	6	7	8	5	9	2	1	4
8	5	2	4	1	7	9	6	3
4	9	1	3	6	2	5	7	8
9	1	4	7	8	6	3	5	2
5	8	3	1	2	4	6	9	7
2	7	6	9	3	5	8	4	1
1	3	9	5	7	8	4	2	6
7	2	5	6	4	3	1	8	9
6	4	8	2	9	1	7	3	5

Sudoku #8

2	1	6	5	8	7	9	4	3
5	3	4	9	6	2	1	7	8
7	9	8	4	1	3	5	6	2
6	5	2	8	3	4	7	1	9
8	7	9	2	5	1	6	3	4
3	4	1	6	7	9	8	2	5
1	2	5	3	9	6	4	8	7
4	8	7	1	2	5	3	9	6
9	6	3	7	4	8	2	5	1

Sudoku #9

1	9	2	4	7	3	8	6	5
6	3	5	1	2	8	9	7	4
8	7	4	9	6	5	1	2	3
5	6	1	8	9	7	3	4	2
4	8	3	2	1	6	5	9	7
9	2	7	5	3	4	6	8	1
2	4	9	6	5	1	7	3	8
3	5	6	7	8	2	4	1	9
7	1	8	3	4	9	2	5	6

Sudoku #10

8	4	9	7	5	3	2	6	1
1	3	5	2	8	6	9	7	4
7	2	6	4	9	1	5	3	8
6	9	2	1	3	8	7	4	5
4	7	8	5	6	2	1	9	3
3	5	1	9	4	7	6	8	2
5	1	3	6	7	4	8	2	9
2	8	7	3	1	9	4	5	6
9	6	4	8	2	5	3	1	7

Sudoku #11

9	3	8	7	6	1	4	2	5
6	1	2	5	4	8	9	3	7
4	7	5	2	9	3	6	8	1
3	8	4	6	7	5	2	1	9
7	5	1	8	2	9	3	4	6
2	9	6	3	1	4	7	5	8
8	2	9	1	3	7	5	6	4
1	4	3	9	5	6	8	7	2
5	6	7	4	8	2	1	9	3

Sudoku #12

5	1	3	2	8	4	7	9	6
6	9	4	3	1	7	5	2	8
8	2	7	9	6	5	3	1	4
4	5	8	1	9	6	2	3	7
2	3	1	7	5	8	4	6	9
7	6	9	4	3	2	1	8	5
9	8	2	5	7	3	6	4	1
3	7	6	8	4	1	9	5	2
1	4	5	6	2	9	8	7	3

Sudoku #13

7	2	8	3	1	4	9	5	6
4	3	6	5	7	9	8	2	1
1	5	9	6	8	2	3	4	7
6	9	2	4	3	7	5	1	8
3	7	1	2	5	8	4	6	9
8	4	5	9	6	1	7	3	2
9	6	4	7	2	5	1	8	3
5	1	3	8	9	6	2	7	4
2	8	7	1	4	3	6	9	5

Sudoku #14

6	8	3	1	7	2	5	4	9
9	2	4	5	8	6	1	3	7
5	7	1	3	9	4	8	6	2
2	4	6	8	1	7	3	9	5
1	9	5	4	2	3	6	7	8
7	3	8	9	6	5	4	2	1
8	5	2	6	3	9	7	1	4
3	1	7	2	4	8	9	5	6
4	6	9	7	5	1	2	8	3

Sudoku #15

7	1	8	4	6	5	2	3	9
2	4	6	3	1	9	7	8	5
5	3	9	8	2	7	4	1	6
3	9	2	1	5	6	8	7	4
4	8	5	2	7	3	6	9	1
6	7	1	9	4	8	5	2	3
1	6	7	5	9	2	3	4	8
8	5	4	7	3	1	9	6	2
9	2	3	6	8	4	1	5	7

Sudoku #16

5	1	4	3	7	9	8	2	6
6	2	8	1	5	4	3	9	7
9	7	3	8	6	2	1	4	5
1	9	6	5	4	8	7	3	2
4	3	7	2	9	1	5	6	8
8	5	2	7	3	6	4	1	9
7	4	5	6	2	3	9	8	1
3	6	1	9	8	7	2	5	4
2	8	9	4	1	5	6	7	3

Sudoku #17

3	4	1	9	8	7	6	2	5
7	6	8	5	2	1	4	3	9
2	9	5	3	6	4	8	7	1
5	8	3	7	9	6	1	4	2
6	1	2	4	3	8	5	9	7
9	7	4	2	1	5	3	8	6
1	3	7	6	4	2	9	5	8
4	2	6	8	5	9	7	1	3
8	5	9	1	7	3	2	6	4

Sudoku #18

2	4	9	5	6	1	8	7	3
1	5	3	8	2	7	9	4	6
8	7	6	4	3	9	1	5	2
5	9	2	7	1	8	6	3	4
6	1	4	2	5	3	7	9	8
7	3	8	9	4	6	2	1	5
9	2	5	1	8	4	3	6	7
4	6	7	3	9	2	5	8	1
3	8	1	6	7	5	4	2	9

Sudoku #19

8	7	5	9	6	3	4	1	2
1	3	9	2	4	7	8	5	6
6	2	4	5	8	1	3	9	7
7	6	1	8	2	4	5	3	9
9	5	8	7	3	6	1	2	4
3	4	2	1	9	5	6	7	8
2	8	3	6	1	9	7	4	5
4	9	7	3	5	8	2	6	1
5	1	6	4	7	2	9	8	3

Sudoku #20

6	5	3	9	2	8	1	7	4
8	7	2	4	1	6	5	9	3
4	1	9	5	3	7	2	6	8
2	8	6	1	9	5	3	4	7
1	9	5	7	4	3	8	2	6
3	4	7	6	8	2	9	1	5
5	2	1	8	6	4	7	3	9
9	6	8	3	7	1	4	5	2
7	3	4	2	5	9	6	8	1

Sudoku #21

7	4	9	5	8	6	1	3	2
3	5	6	1	2	7	4	8	9
1	8	2	4	9	3	5	7	6
5	6	1	7	3	4	2	9	8
9	2	7	8	6	1	3	4	5
4	3	8	9	5	2	6	1	7
8	9	3	6	4	5	7	2	1
6	7	4	2	1	8	9	5	3
2	1	5	3	7	9	8	6	4

Sudoku #22

3	9	1	4	2	6	5	8	7
7	4	5	3	8	9	6	1	2
8	6	2	5	7	1	9	3	4
2	8	3	7	4	5	1	6	9
4	1	6	9	3	2	8	7	5
5	7	9	1	6	8	4	2	3
9	3	8	6	5	7	2	4	1
1	2	7	8	9	4	3	5	6
6	5	4	2	1	3	7	9	8

Sudoku #23

9	3	8	1	7	4	5	2	6
7	1	2	5	8	6	3	4	9
4	5	6	2	9	3	1	8	7
3	7	4	8	2	5	9	6	1
6	2	9	4	1	7	8	3	5
1	8	5	3	6	9	2	7	4
8	4	7	9	5	2	6	1	3
2	9	3	6	4	1	7	5	8
5	6	1	7	3	8	4	9	2

Sudoku #24

3	5	9	7	8	1	2	6	4
6	8	7	2	9	4	3	1	5
2	1	4	6	5	3	9	8	7
8	3	6	4	7	2	1	5	9
4	9	1	5	6	8	7	3	2
5	7	2	1	3	9	8	4	6
9	2	5	8	1	6	4	7	3
7	4	8	3	2	5	6	9	1
1	6	3	9	4	7	5	2	8

Sudoku #25

5	3	2	6	7	4	1	9	8
4	1	9	8	3	5	7	6	2
7	8	6	9	1	2	3	4	5
3	7	1	2	6	8	9	5	4
9	4	8	3	5	7	2	1	6
6	2	5	1	4	9	8	3	7
1	5	3	7	2	6	4	8	9
8	6	7	4	9	3	5	2	1
2	9	4	5	8	1	6	7	3

Sudoku #26

4	8	3	5	9	6	7	1	2
6	1	7	4	2	3	8	9	5
9	5	2	1	7	8	6	4	3
3	6	5	2	4	7	9	8	1
7	9	1	8	6	5	3	2	4
2	4	8	9	3	1	5	6	7
8	3	4	7	1	9	2	5	6
1	7	9	6	5	2	4	3	8
5	2	6	3	8	4	1	7	9

Sudoku #27

5	1	2	7	4	3	8	6	9
4	8	3	9	5	6	2	1	7
9	6	7	2	8	1	3	5	4
1	9	4	3	6	2	5	7	8
2	7	6	8	1	5	4	9	3
8	3	5	4	9	7	6	2	1
6	2	8	1	7	4	9	3	5
3	4	1	5	2	9	7	8	6
7	5	9	6	3	8	1	4	2

Sudoku #28

7	6	2	8	3	5	1	9	4
9	8	5	4	1	6	3	7	2
4	1	3	2	9	7	6	8	5
3	7	8	6	5	1	2	4	9
5	2	6	3	4	9	7	1	8
1	4	9	7	8	2	5	3	6
6	9	4	1	2	3	8	5	7
8	3	7	5	6	4	9	2	1
2	5	1	9	7	8	4	6	3

Sudoku #29

2	6	9	4	8	7	3	1	5
4	7	1	3	5	2	8	9	6
3	8	5	6	9	1	7	4	2
8	1	2	9	4	3	5	6	7
7	5	3	1	6	8	9	2	4
6	9	4	2	7	5	1	8	3
9	4	8	7	3	6	2	5	1
5	2	7	8	1	4	6	3	9
1	3	6	5	2	9	4	7	8

Sudoku #30

8	2	5	7	6	1	4	3	9
6	9	3	8	4	2	5	1	7
1	7	4	5	9	3	8	2	6
7	3	9	2	5	6	1	4	8
2	4	6	1	3	8	9	7	5
5	1	8	9	7	4	2	6	3
3	8	2	6	1	5	7	9	4
9	6	1	4	8	7	3	5	2
4	5	7	3	2	9	6	8	1

Sudoku #31

7	4	3	6	2	1	9	5	8
1	6	2	8	5	9	4	3	7
9	5	8	4	3	7	6	1	2
6	9	1	3	7	4	8	2	5
3	8	5	2	9	6	7	4	1
2	7	4	5	1	8	3	9	6
4	2	9	7	8	5	1	6	3
5	1	7	9	6	3	2	8	4
8	3	6	1	4	2	5	7	9

Sudoku #32

6	7	1	8	3	4	5	9	2
8	3	2	9	6	5	4	7	1
4	9	5	1	2	7	8	3	6
3	1	6	2	7	8	9	5	4
2	5	4	3	9	6	7	1	8
7	8	9	4	5	1	2	6	3
9	6	3	5	8	2	1	4	7
5	4	8	7	1	3	6	2	9
1	2	7	6	4	9	3	8	5

Sudoku #33

7	9	1	5	2	8	3	6	4
8	4	2	6	3	7	9	1	5
6	3	5	4	1	9	8	7	2
9	5	7	2	4	1	6	8	3
3	1	4	8	7	6	2	5	9
2	8	6	3	9	5	7	4	1
5	6	9	1	8	2	4	3	7
1	7	3	9	6	4	5	2	8
4	2	8	7	5	3	1	9	6

Sudoku #34

3	7	6	4	1	9	5	8	2
2	1	4	5	3	8	6	7	9
9	5	8	7	2	6	1	4	3
7	6	2	9	4	1	8	3	5
5	8	9	2	6	3	4	1	7
1	4	3	8	5	7	9	2	6
8	3	7	6	9	4	2	5	1
4	9	5	1	7	2	3	6	8
6	2	1	3	8	5	7	9	4

Sudoku #35

3	8	7	9	4	6	2	1	5
6	5	9	3	1	2	8	7	4
4	1	2	5	7	8	6	3	9
7	4	3	8	9	1	5	2	6
5	6	8	2	3	7	4	9	1
2	9	1	6	5	4	3	8	7
8	7	4	1	2	5	9	6	3
1	3	6	4	8	9	7	5	2
9	2	5	7	6	3	1	4	8

Sudoku #36

4	1	5	7	2	9	6	8	3
6	7	9	8	5	3	4	1	2
2	3	8	4	6	1	5	7	9
9	8	6	2	1	5	3	4	7
7	5	1	3	4	6	2	9	8
3	2	4	9	8	7	1	5	6
1	4	7	6	9	2	8	3	5
5	6	3	1	7	8	9	2	4
8	9	2	5	3	4	7	6	1

Mitchell Allen is a life-long puzzle enthusiast, story-teller and programmer. One day, he decided that it would be cool to mash all three hobbies into one mad creation. You are holding it. If you, too, appreciate cleverly crafted puzzles mixed in with your classic wordplay staples, you'll love the kinds of puzzles and activities Mitchell has planned.

Follow Mitchell on Twitter (@Anklebuster) and on his website, PencilPaperParacosm.com.

Made in the USA
Monee, IL
14 September 2022